" Remember to look up at the stars and not down at your feet. Try to make sense of what you see and wonder about what makes the Universe exist. Be curious. "

Stephen Hawking

The Master Theorem

ELITE

A book of puzzles, intrigue, and wit

By: M

Printed in USA
ISBN 978-0-578-79979-7

Special thanks to

Shaun Salzberg

Andrew Gibbs

James Gibbs

Stephanie M. McPherson

Chris "Fulminous" Michaud

Frances Rucker & Elizabeth Patterson

Dixon Patten and Bayila Creative

Contents

The Search for the Elite

Imagine: A puff of smoke. Gasps of excitement. A lone street light illuminating a triumphant figure reemerging from the shadows.

Did you miss me?

When we last left our hero (that'd be me), I'd just led you down the winding and mysterious path that was your own mind, unlocking secret potential you scarcely knew existed.

But what if I told you there was more? That you could go higher, further, faster?

I'm M, or at least that's how you know me, and I'll be your guide.

I founded The Master Theorem long ago, as a secret society at my beloved alma mater. We've branched out since those early days of hushed meetings in dank Hogwarts-like rooms. But the aim remains the same—assemble a group of the world's best problem solvers, those out-of-the-box thinkers we so desperately need to steer the course of human civilization. I partly achieved that goal when I found you. You proved your mettle by completing my first puzzling publication and earned yourself membership into our ranks. Bravo.

But a lot has happened since we last spoke: Wildfires. A global pandemic. Harry and Meghan stepping away from the royal family.

So now, it's time to level up. As the world grows more complicated, so does my search for the elite of the elite. Your mission, should you choose to accept it: find the word or phrase solution to each one of my puzzles, called Theorems. Doing so will be your ticket into the upper echelons of The Master Theorem. It's not going to be easy, nor should it be. But to quote one of the greatest sports movies of all time, the hard is what makes it great.

Getting Reacquainted

If my first book was hiking Pikes Peak, this one is more like free soloing El Capitan. The basics are the same—grueling tests of strength at dizzying elevations—but one is a little more, shall we say, perilous than the other.

You have a few questions. Let me take a stab at preempting the initial dialogue.

You: Do I have to complete book one before tackling book two?
Me: No.

You: Should I pick up book one anyways at some point?
Me: Definitely.

You: What exactly are Theorems again?
Me: *Sigh*

The TLDR is: **Theorems are puzzles with a word or phrase answer**, pulled from the many and varied worlds of science, engineering, math, art, and cryptography. There are 40 of them this time around, but if you're looking for more guidance than that, you're out of luck. There's no one way to tackle a Theorem, so just think like an expert detective, follow the logic, and, well, you know what they say: when you have eliminated the impossible, whatever remains, however improbable, must be the truth.

But you're no Sherlock Holmes yet, so I won't cast you into the darkest night without a lamp to light your way. **Each Theorem comes with three hints** to point you in the right direction, should you need them. You'll find the page number where they live at the bottom of each Theorem. Hints are ordered from most coy to most blunt, so when you're just kinda stuck, start with #1. When you're about to throw the book out the window, it might be time for #3. Or a glass of scotch.

Either way, my hints are encrypted with a simple shift so you can avoid seeing something you'll wish you hadn't. To decode, just move each letter one forward: A turns into B, B turns into C, Z turns into A, et cetera et cetera and so forth. For you short-cut takers out there, there's a handy-dandy auto-decoder at **http://themastertheorem.com/hints**.

But here I am, rambling on and on about hints when you obviously won't need them. Silly me.

Full solutions to each Theorem can be found in the back of the book, on the page number shown at the bottom of each Theorem. But before you break out your celebratory touchdown dance, realize that your hard-fought "answer" might still be a few yards away from the end zone. So avoid epic spoilers by always heading to **http://themastertheorem.com/solutions** first, where you can double check if what you've got is right before seeing what actually is.

Oh, and as you're puzzling your way through, feel free to scribble away on my Theorems with all your thoughts, charts, codes, and diagrams. You know, *Beautiful Mind*-style. Or, if you are loath to deface my book, I've included a Notes section in the back. It's just a bunch of blank pages, so go to town.

Just remember: you're not in this alone. There's a whole community of like-minded Members attempting this very quest. Create kinship with your fellow knights at the round table by heading to **http://themastertheorem.com/forums** anytime to trade insights, answer questions, or debate the air-speed velocity of an unladen swallow.

And now, I release you into the wondrous world of Theorems. I've put training wheels on the first few lest you immediately crash into a mailbox. But after that, it will be full speed ahead.

Allons-y!

Training Theorems

"Tell me and I forget, teach
me and I may remember,
involve me and I learn."

Benjamin Franklin

Learning to Count

You're new at this, so let's try something: Imagine you're back in your childhood living room. The TV's inches from your face and the *Sesame Street* gang just got going in their daily exploration of letters and numbers. Bert and Ernie belting out the ABCs. The Count tallying up everything from chickens to telephone rings. You're enthralled by that cape. That epic widow's peak!

Now follow the throughline from those Sunny Days to your grown up life and this very book. Hopefully you've realized how instrumental those early run-ins with numbers and letters really were. For when their powers combine, it's like knowing a magic phrase that opens your fledgling mind to bigger, better, and more puzzling experiences.

This is today,
M

TIP

The tales of triumph accompanying each puzzle, or Theorem, are not just for your entertainment. **Always comb my words for subtle clues** about what to do.

TIP

Here's the puzzle itself. Remember that one way or another, **the solution will come in the form of a word or phrase**. Give it a shot—I've gone easy on you this time.

Theorem-Solving Skill #1: Converting Numbers to Letters

When you see a bunch of numbers or letters, try translating them from one to the other, where A is 1, B is 2, Z is 26, and everything in between. Basically, **think of A - Z and 1 - 26 as interchangeable**.

15 16 5 14

19 5 19 1 13 5

TIP

I often **like using red** to mean, "Hey, look here for the final answer."

TIP

Once you've got this Theorem down for the count, turn the page and try the next one.

Bookworms Anonymous

My name is M, and I'm a bookworm.

I have a top-three list for every genre and subgenre you can think of. Bangsian? Check. Bildungsroman? Got you covered. Solarpunk? You bet. But of course this stargazer is partial to popsci astrophysics.

Like a rocketship through spacetime, I bore through books about our universe faster than the speed of light. *Fabric of the Cosmos* by Brain Greene. *Parallel Worlds* by Michio Kaku. *Welcome to the Universe* by Neil deGrasse Tyson. *Pale Blue Dot* by Carl Sagan. I mean, Brian, Michio, Neil, and Carl are like my John, Paul, George, and Ringo.

But there are more neuron-stretching nuggets of knowledge in just one of these books than atoms in the observable universe. So to keep things organized, you really have to make good use of the book's index. Simply grab the page number to pick out the gem you're looking for, then sit back, relax, and ponder the workings of the universe.

This is today,
M

TIP
You probably don't need it right now, but **try decoding the hints on this page** anyway. Practice makes perfect, and you'll need this skill down the line.

TIP
Solved it already? Then **check out the full solution on this page**. Even if you think you nailed it, it'll still be enlightening to hear my take on things.

Hints: 100 • **Solution:** 122 • **Forum:** theorems.help/bookworms

Theorem-Solving Skill #2: Indexing, Ordering, and Grouping

Numbers you encounter won't always spell out a word on their own. Instead, they might be telling you to **pick a certain letter out of a word (called "indexing"), order letters in a certain way, or group letters into words**—whatever the Theorem implies.

REALLY TINY,
DEPRESSINGLY SMALL
BLUE DOT
BY KARL ZAGAN

INDEX

PART I

PART II

___ ___ ___ ___   ___ ___ ___ ___

3   4   1   2   4   2   1   3

Citizens of the Earth

On occasion, I find myself sent abroad for my work. You know how business trips can be. It's mostly the drudgery of outrunning well-funded miscreants in a souped-up car and not much sightseeing. But I do my best to leave at least one evening free of heart-pounding action to soak in the culture of whatever country I'm "visiting".

When you travel as much as I do, you realize it's a shame that the nearly 200 countries of the world give us these beautifully diverse cultures, but remain separated by arbitrary geopolitical boundaries. It'd do such wonders for the world to tear down those walls and bring everyone together under one flag. We just need a way to keep the food and song and dance of each individual place while at the same time joining hands as one big happy family.

This is today,
M

TIP
Don't forget to **read my ramblings for clues**. But don't get hyper-focused on any one thing either. Sometimes I say things just because I want to.

TIP
Feel free to use the pages of this book to work through your ideas. **Write or draw anywhere** necessary to get the job done.

Hints: 100 • **Solution:** 124 • **Forum:** theorems.help/citizens

Theorem-Solving Skill #3: Using the Internet

While encyclopedic knowledge and a photographic memory would be helpful, I don't expect that of you quite yet. So if you don't know something, **it's always acceptable to google** it. Just don't get lost down any clickholes.

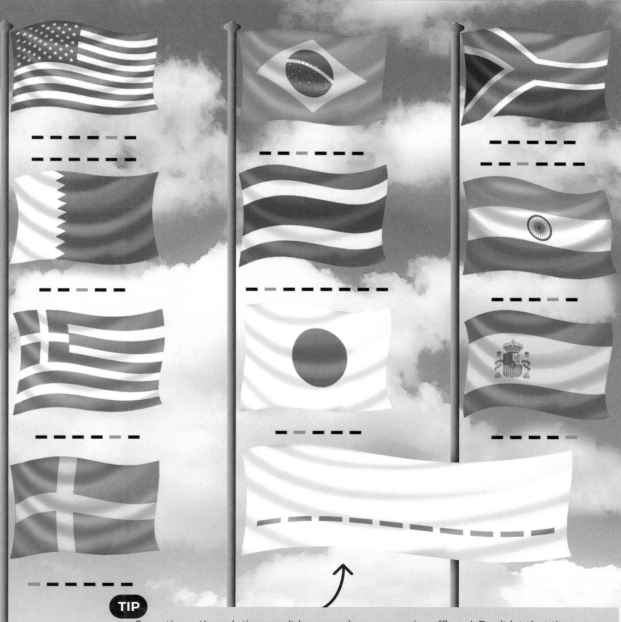

TIP

Sometimes the solution won't be a word you recognize offhand. Don't let that throw you. **Check your answer online first** before driving yourself crazy looking for something else.

Subbing Tires for Tiramisu

One of the many perks about getting to travel the world is the sheer number of cuisines I've been able to try. So as you can imagine, I've become a bit of a foodie. At this point, I've made it to almost all of the nearly 3,000 restaurants in the world rated with Michelin Stars (which, if you're not familiar, is like the Rotten Tomatoes of the restaurant world, but much more posh).

The hilarious thing is that these elite ratings were actually started in the early 1900s by tire manufacturers. You got that right—the one with the logo made of tires that kind of looks like the Stay Puft Marshmallow Man.

Where those Michelin brothers got their food expertise is a real cipher to me. I mean, going from tires to haute cuisine—talk about an upgrade! So next time I'm at one of these chic restaurants, I plan to ask for a pricey item substitution. I'm sure they won't mind; that kind of switch is in their DNA.

This is today,
M

TIP
I know you love tediously decoding my hints, but save yourself some time and use the hint auto-decoder at:
http://themastertheorem.com/hints

TIP
Avoid glimpsing a spoiler in the back of the book. Always first check to see if your answer is correct at:
http://themastertheorem.com/solutions

Hints: 101 • **Solution:** 126 • **Forum:** theorems.help/tiramisu

Theorem-Solving Skill #4: Decoding Ciphers

Get familiar with the many different types of ciphers—or methods of encoding—that exist in the world. **Keep an eye out for visual and textual hints that point to a particular cipher**, and as always, google when you need to.

Cypher Restaurant

On the menu tonight:

ANCHOVY*

*Substitutions allowed and encouraged!
L D B Z G N H S V K A W M O T J F Y C U X E Q P R I

TIP

You'll probably need to keep notes as you're decoding, so **make use of the Notes section**. You can find it in the back of the book.

A Leap of Faith

Sometimes, things just go wrong.

We've all been there, right? Power outages right before you hit save on your group presentation. Forgetting to charge your camera battery before a photo club expedition. Comms going out when you're infiltrating the high-rise office building of a secretive bioweapons manufacturer right when you need to confirm your extraction point with your team.

When the going gets tough, you have to get creative. Think outside the box—or maximum security lab space, as it were. No comms link? Simply hold up an old school paper note to the window as your teammate rappels down the building to respond through the glass.

When all else fails, remember to think on your feet, trust in yourself and your team, and sometimes, take a leap of faith.

This is today,
M

TIP

If you're still stumped after using the hints, think I've made a mistake (unlikely), or just want to nerd out with other members, **check out the online forum for this Theorem** by going here.

↓

Hints: 101 · **Solution:** 128 · **Forum:** theorems.help/leap

Theorem-Solving Skill #5: Thinking Outside the Box

Sometimes you'll have to do a bit more than just rearrange letters on a page. So if you're feeling stuck, remember to **think outside the box**. Get creative, trust your gut, and do whatever you need to do to get the job done.

extraction point 2.

Theorems

"Somewhere, something
incredible is waiting
to be known."

Carl Sagan

TMT 2: The Second One

Sequels get a bad rap sometimes, and your expectations must be sky high after the thrill ride that was my first book. Rest assured, *TMT: Elite* is no *Caddyshack II*—I'd like to think it's more along the lines of *The Empire Strikes Back*. But instead of a wise green alien guiding your spiritual growth, you get me.

The thing with second installments is they have to be saying something. If you're just putting out another book or movie as a cash grab, people will be able to tell. Purpose, drive, and narrative are key to hooking your audience and holding on to them through new sets of trials and tribulations.

So, what's my purpose and drive this time, you ask? What am I trying to say with this Master Theorem sequel? Great questions. Are you elite enough to find out?

This is today,

M

Hints: 101 • **Solution:** 130 • **Forum:** theorems.help/tmt2

THE HITCHHIKER'S GUIDE TO THE GALAXY   THE _____

RAIDERS OF THE LOST ARK   _____

OCEAN'S ELEVEN   ____ _____

THE BOURNE IDENTITY   THE _____ _____

DR. NO   ____ ___ ___

THE NOTEBOOK   THE _____

A Foreign Exchange

There's a lot that spy movies get wrong. Certain things they'd have you think are everyday occurrences just aren't that common. I mean, I can count on one hand the number of times I've crashed a fundraising event for a seemingly benevolent charity that's really a front for a devious evildoer bent on creating a water monopoly.

But one thing they always seem to get right is the secret stash of passports and foreign currency that make for an easy getaway. With a new ID, some local cash, and a bit of stick-on facial hair, I can quickly convert from a humble Swiss chocolatier to a South African opera star touring in Japan.

But it does have the potential to confuse the heck out of your everyday criminals, like that time I disarmed my would-be mugger in a St. Petersburg alley. During the scuffle, some Uzbekistani and Korean money tumbled from my pockets along with a few of my passports. A hilarious look of horror spread across his face as he realized he chose the wrong victim, and he just gasped, "Who *are* you?!"

I have to say, my response was witty, even for me.

This is today,
M

1 JOD : 5 ILS   1 CNY : 1 GTQ

1 INR : 0.1 GTQ   1 CNY : 16 JPY

1 AED : 32 JPY   1 CHF : 77.5 INR

1 JOD : 25 ZAR   1 JOD : 12.4 GTQ

1 HRK : 16 JPY   1 BRL : 0.6 AED

1 JPY : 0.7 RUB

Glitches in the Matrix

When you notice three identical cars drive by in a row, or when the chirping of a bird sounds too rhythmic and repeating, you have to wonder if we aren't living in some kind of *Matrix*-like simulation.

I have to admit, I'm pretty fascinated by the theory that everything we experience amounts to one big computer program, and we're nothing more than bits of code. If that's true, then nothing around us is real. Not the book you are holding, not the keyboard I'm typing on, not the painting of a pipe on my wall that declares "*Ceci n'est pas une pipe.*"

And it's not just a leather-clad Keanu Reeves fighting octopus-like machines for the future of humanity that'd have you believe that.

Some philosophers claim this simulation hypothesis is not only possible but likely. Think about it: if advanced civilizations inevitably create simulated societies, then perhaps those simulated civilizations—once advanced enough—would create more simulations. This would keep happening down the line until most of the conscious minds in the universe would be simulated. And what's so special about us that we'd be the one original, biological civilization rather than one of the infinite simulations?

That's enough to send anyone into an existential spiral, but the thought is kind of freeing, too. If there is nothing but code, then theoretically you could learn to find patterns in that code and bend the perceived laws of physics to your will. Like Neo dodging bullets and taking off from phone booths Superman-style.

But I don't know. Things just feel too real to be fake. Or is that what Agent Smith wants me to think?

This is today,
M

Hints: 102 • **Solution:** 134 • **Forum:** theorems.help/matrix

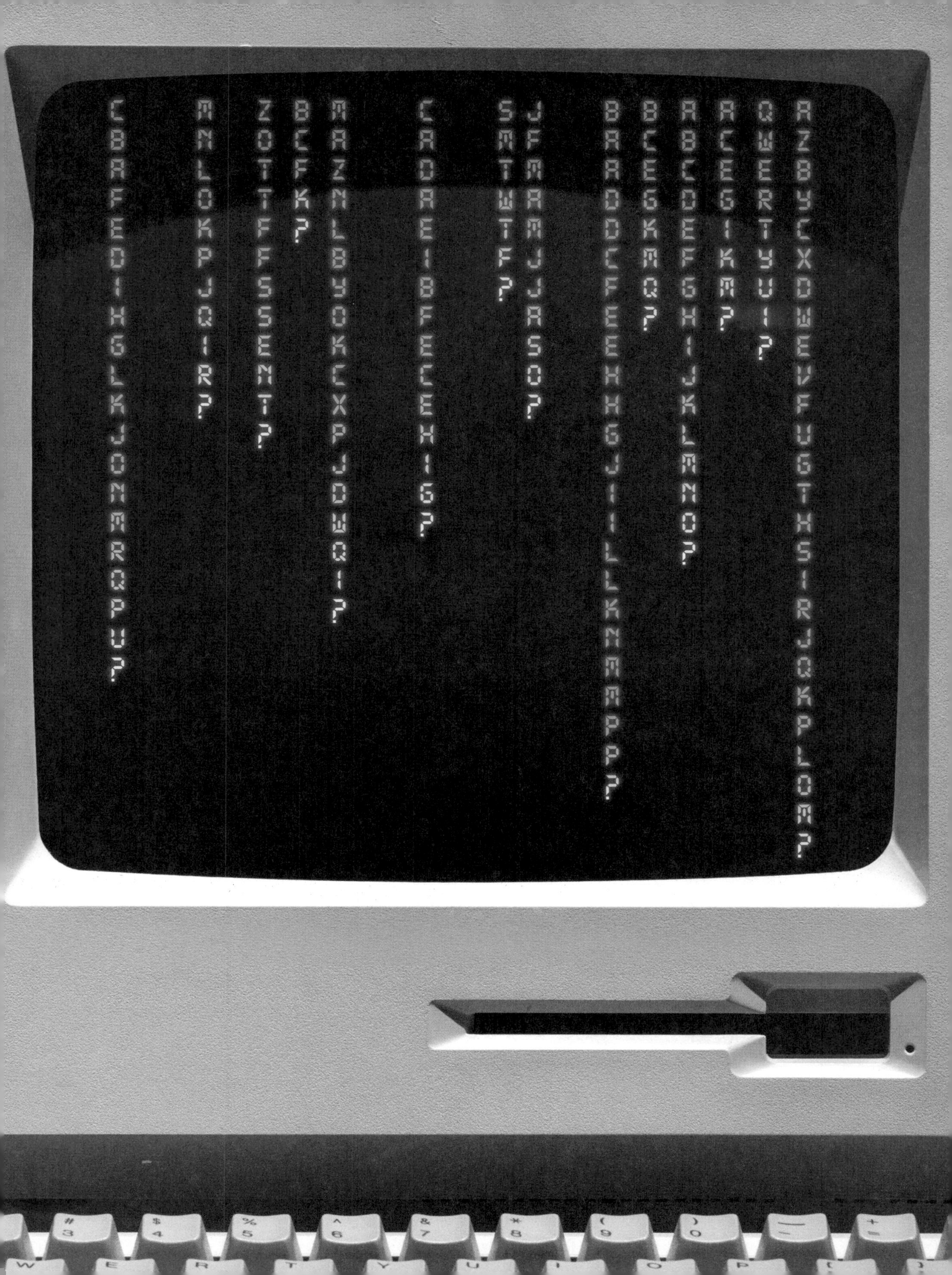

CBRAFEDIHGLKJONMRQPUP

MNLOKPJQIRP

ZOTTFFSSENTP

BACFKP?

MAZNLBYOKCXPJDWQIP

CADRAEIBFECEXIGP?

SJMNTWTFP?
MRJASOP

BRADCFEEHGJILLKNMMPPP

BCEGKMQP

ABCDEFGHIJKLMNOP

ACEGIKMP?

QWERTYUIP?

AZBYCXDWEVFUGTHSIRJQKPLOMP

Do the Doppler Shift

No matter who you are or what you do, it helps to know physics. Like that time some henchmen were chasing me in a stolen ice cream truck and I had to hide behind a garbage bin in an alleyway to wait for it to pass by. You know the tip off, right? As a sound moves towards you, it gets higher-pitched than usual and as it moves away it gets lower-pitched, because science. With an ice cream truck, the effect is so distinctive—that jolly jingle echoing merrily as it approaches you before shifting to a lower pitch that turns the now receding tune dark and demonic.

Ah, the good old Doppler shift, signaling to spies that the coast is clear since...well, since the beginning of the universe really. See, it's not just sound affected by this phenomenon. It also happens with light in the universe. When galaxies are moving towards Earth, the light they emit is "blueshifted," since the wavelength of the emitted spectrum gets squished a little (when compared to a stationary reference sample) and becomes a little bluer. Galaxies moving away from Earth are "redshifted" since the wavelength of their light gets stretched and becomes redder.

Interestingly, almost all galaxies in the universe are redshifted, indicating they are almost all moving away from Earth—something scientists have taken as solid evidence that the universe is expanding at an accelerating rate, with galaxies being pushed away from each other by a mysterious force permeating all of space.

If only I could harness that power when trying to make one of my daring escapes. Hiding with garbage while waiting for the sounds of the Dark Lord's Ice Cream Truck isn't very dignified.

This is today,
M

Hints: 103 • **Solution:** 136 • **Forum:** theorems.help/doppler

Galaxy Spectral Survey

Unshifted Reference Spectrum

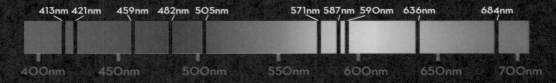

413nm 421nm 459nm 482nm 505nm   571nm 587nm 590nm 636nm   684nm

400nm   450nm   500nm   550nm   600nm   650nm   700nm

Inventing Hope

I have a lot of ideas. Too many, some would say.

There's a 97-page document on my computer dating back decades that's chock full of concepts for products and services and technologies, each idea clearly jealous of its select few peers I've actually had the time to execute on. They're all over the place, too. A new type of ergonomic chair. A plan for stopping hurricanes. A concept for the next big dating app. An algorithm for harnessing the regular pulses of quasars to create a universal positioning system for when interstellar travel finally becomes possible.

Most of my ideas are too advanced for the current state of physics. Some are little more than quirky Rube Goldberg machines made for my own entertainment. But a glorious few *are* doable—*and* have the potential to save the world.

I'm not being hyperbolic here. Take my latest invention. The climate is changing and all the trash and junk we generate as a wasteful species is choking out the Earth and its oceans. Plain old reducing, reusing and recycling can only do so much. So to combat this, I've created (drumroll, please...) the Matter Sorter!

Don't judge, it's just a working name.

It kind of looks like a garbage can you'd find on the Starship Enterprise. You throw in any trash—any matter, really—and the machine breaks it all down into its constituent atoms, then sorts those atoms based on type. Toss in an old cellphone and out comes blocks of copper, nickel, silicon, and dozens of other elements, all neatly arranged for reuse as raw materials. What we've got here, folks, is a perfectly efficient recycling machine.

See, engineering is all about inventing a brighter future for ourselves. We talk about saving the Earth, but what we mean is saving the Earth as we know it. The Earth itself will always bounce back, one way or another. Whether or not it stays habitable for humans is up to us.

Now all I need is a catchy brand name to get this gadget into every home around the world. Then say goodbye to trash, forever.

This is today,
M

Hints: 103 · **Solution:** 138 · **Forum:** theorems.help/inventing

TABLE SALT

0% Less Sodium Than Normal

Aluminum FOIL

ORGANIC MILK

100% Daily Value of Calcium

ANTISEPTIC
Iodine Solution

THERMOMETER

50 50
40 40
30 30
20 20
10 10
0 0

Caution: Contains Mercury

BOCKYBALLS

Rare Earth Neodymium Magnets

ROLEX
100% Gold

DIETARY SUPPLEMENTS

100 Zinc Caplets

BATTERY
Lithium-ion

2 —
8 —
4 —
7 —
7 —
10 —
8 —
4 —
11 —

SORTING...

Face With Rolling Eyes

I know I give off a killer lone-wolf vibe, but the reality is no one can make it in this world alone. Over the years I've assembled some truly special characters to help me pull off my shenanigans, and I think it's time you all met. As I introduce my crew, I encourage you to imagine an *Ocean's Eleven*-style montage of each individual's unique abilities. (Or a *Real Housewives*-like intro with sassy taglines. Whatever floats your boat.) Here we go:

First we've got N, my right hand assistant and logistics guru. If I need anything—from organizing my bullet journal to scheduling time at the Keck Observatory—N's got me covered.

Next up is O, my media outreach whizz. Faster than a speeding Instagram post, O can get my name in the news—or keep it out, as the case sometimes may be.

Then of course there's P, my tech genius. You can thank P for building **themastertheorem.com** (which you should obviously be frequenting for hints and solutions).

And let's not forget Q, my accounting ninja. His collection of calculating tech from throughout history is good enough to be in the Smithsonian.

Then finally, there's me. I'm a pretty great boss, if I do say so myself. My team and I have got a whole found-family-adventuring-across-the-world vibe going on, a la *Avatar: the Last Airbender*. (Q is for sure third-season Zuko. He may seem quietly moody but when he gets really mad—ho boy, watch out.)

See, that's the thing. Making the workplace feel like home means understanding and balancing the components of everyone's emotions and unique codes of conduct. And a little friendly ribbing doesn't hurt, either.

This is today,
M

O

exciting news, @channel! we pulled some strings with M's connections in the media world... so you may start seeing the books make subtle appearances on prime time...

P

awesome, congrats! will M be making a first appearance on tv, too? 🤪

O

haha, um? no.

P

j/k i'll take a second tomorrow to spin up some more web servers to handle the increased traffic 🍕

N

amazing, @O! i'll submit that third order with our printing facility and get the fulfillment center geared up to ship more books! 👻

O

good idea...

Q

sigh how much is this going to eat out of our fourth quarter profits? 🍀

O

nothing, @Q. people owe M favors... why r u all reacting so weird?

P

I plead the fifth... j/k we're just excited! soon we'll have enough members! 🐟

N

and soon after there will be enough elite! ⬜❓

O

huh? @N, what was that last one? it didn't show up

N

oh, you might not have that one on your computer yet... or do you?

O

hah, you're all ridiculous

Type message here...

B *I* ~~S~~

☺

A Quipu Cousin

Ancient South and Central American civilizations had some pretty impressive mathematical advances. Between the Aztec Codex Vergara for surveying and the exactitude of the Mayan calendar, these folk really knew their way around numbers.

But the early American mathematical system that really draws me is the Quipu from Andean South America. The Inca in particular were masters of this artistic form of accounting and record keeping. The colorful strings filled with patterned knots kept track of detailed data about all sorts of things—the population, taxes, dates, even the military.

Many scholars think the knots only record raw numeric information. But I've done a little digging of my own (literally) in a previously untouched region of the Andes, and I'm pretty sure I've uncovered a whole new branch of Quipu. It's quite remarkable really. Suffice it to say, they did things a little differently from their well-documented cousins.

This is today,
M

Hints: 104 • **Solution:** 142 • **Forum:** theorems.help/quipu

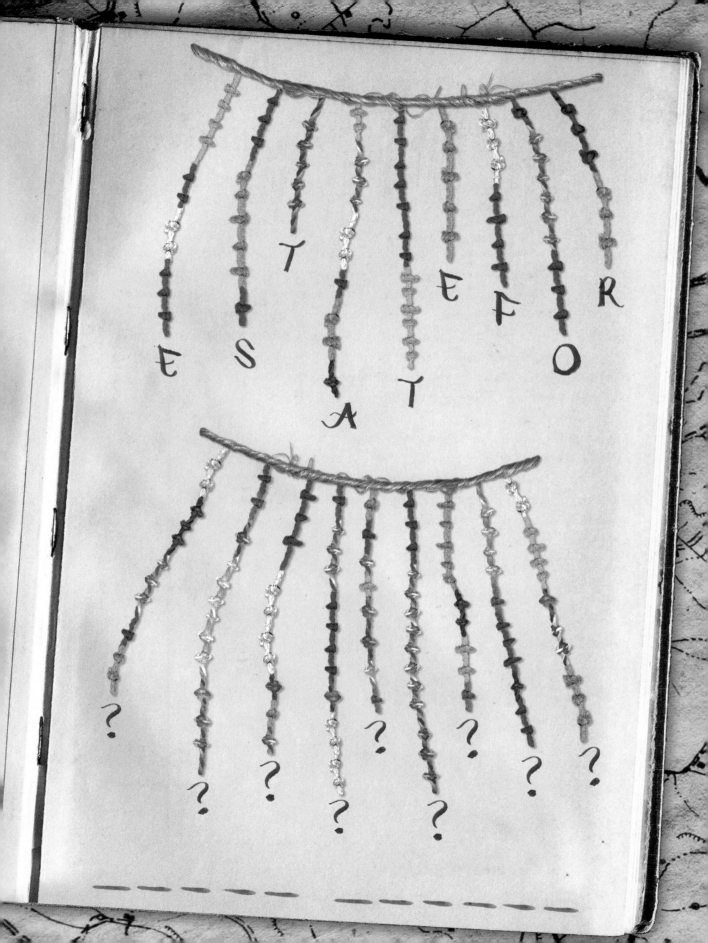

A Tale of Two Killers

Traveling the world is quite inspirational, especially for an up-and-coming mystery writer like myself. The different characters you meet, each with their own distinct features, mannerisms, and life stories open your eyes to all the different paths life has to offer. It's almost like a game, imagining the unlikely sequence of events that brought them all to the exact moment that you spot them. The dapper white haired gent in the fedora pretending to read the news when he's really skimming the obituaries. The bespectacled ginger with the flower hat who walks her pet skunk on a leash. The harsh, cynical eyes of the pencil-thin-mustachioed butcher. I mean, come on! These characters are just begging to be immortalized in print.

As you're likely aware, I've been lucky enough to channel that mental energy into a rewarding career as a murder mystery novelist. (Ahem, you may have heard of such classics as *Who in the Where with the What?* and *L.M. Entarrie*?) Well, I just finished my latest masterpiece, and keep your eyes peeled for more forthcoming! In each, I explore what it means to be an individual in this wild world, question what makes a person act so distinctly, and delve into what could drive someone to...murder.

This is today,
M

A TALE OF TWO KILLERS

By: M

The summer of 1979 was hot and humid. Me and my partner Theo approached a particularly heinous crime scene at dusk, mopping sweat off our brows. The thick air and the fading light almost made the victims look like cartoon figures lying face down in the alley.

"Any witnesses?" I asked the responding cop, an Officer Bradley.

"Dozens," he said. "But their testimony was all over the place. We got reports of glasses, big noses, bald heads, red hair, blue eyes, brown eyes, hats, moustaches, beards. Nothing consistent or usable. Only thing everyone could agree on is that one of our killers was a guy and one was a gal."

"A regular Bonnie and Clyde, eh?" I laughed. "Well, knowing it's a guy doesn't do much for us. But knowing a gal is involved—that'll help us out big."

"Ora, over here!" Theo called. He'd drifted down the alley to take a look around. He used his toe to poke at a large earring on the pavement. "Must be from our Bonnie. And take a look at that." He pointed to a strand of red hair on one of the vics, shining with what must have been some beard or moustache oil. "From our Clyde, most likely."

We rounded up the witnesses and, with their help and the talents of our sketch artist, Milton, drew up the faces of 24 possible suspects. They were the traditional lot—not a particularly diverse group of people, but all with very distinct looks, which was enough to round up 48 people who matched the descriptions to bring them in for questioning.

We divvied up the suspects—24 for Theo and 24 for me. Theo brought his into the Blue room for questioning. He figures the blue puts the suspects more at ease, makes 'em more likely to answer questions. But me, I like 'em riled up. On edge. That's why I put mine in the Red interrogation room.

I gave Theo the benefit of first questioning; him being one year younger than me, I like to give him an edge when I can. We volleyed back and forth, taking turns questioning the witnesses and eliminating suspects as we went on. They were dropping like flies.

By the end of the day, Theo had confirmed our male suspect also had blue eyes. I'd determined the other wore a hat in a pathetic attempt at a disguise. It may not have seemed like much, but that was all the information we needed. We left the final few suspects dangling in their interrogation rooms while we reported in to the Chief of Police.

"New record for me, Chief. With just four pieces of witness testimony, I'm confident I know the guy who helped commit these murders," Theo said smugly.

I chuckled a little. "You've got a lot to learn, kid. I had our dame pegged after only three pieces of evidence. So I win, I guess.

The Chief wasn't amused. "Quit it, you two. This isn't a game, so don't make me guess who did it. Just tell me who.

Mystery Ongoing

Imagine you're a night security guard, strolling along the moonlit hallways of an art museum, taking in the grandeur of Rembrandt and Degas when two police officers knock on the door. You answer, right?

Well, you'd make a terrible security guard. One guard at the Isabella Stewart Gardner Museum learned that the hard way back in 1990 when the night ended with him and his colleague tied to a chair and the police impersonators spiriting away thirteen priceless pieces of art worth about $500 million.

Now, all thieves have their own peculiar methods of operating, but these were certainly not the methods of well-seasoned art thieves. Sure, they disguised themselves fine enough—complete with cop uniforms and fake moustaches—but there were also major oddities in the way they went about things. The thieves took some minor works while ignoring some of the most important examples of Renaissance art. They used a blade to cut the paintings from their frames, materially damaging them and reducing their value. They quit unscrewing a frame from the wall halfway through because…who knows? They got bored?

You'd think such a peculiarly inelegant thievery would have been easy to solve. But there have never been any real clues. The works never appeared on the black market. They simply disappeared without a trace.

Well, there is one trace. Thanks to the strict stipulation in Gardner's will that nothing about the paintings or artworks in her museum could ever be changed, their empty frames still hang in the places the paintings once occupied as a testament to the lost art. One hopes that if there's no chance of them being restored to their rightful place, at least they're being appreciated in some disreputable art connoisseur's mansion.

Not mine though. No, those are just replicas.

This is today,
M

Hints: 105 • **Solution:** 146 • **Forum:** theorems.help/heist

CHRIS IN THE STORM ON THE SEA OF GALILHEE REMBERANDT

CHEZ TORTOWNI MANET

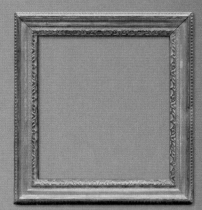

THE CONCERTA VEYRMEER

LEAVING PADDOCK DEGAS

A LAD AND GENTLEWOMAN IN BLACK REMBRANDT

LANDSCAPER WITH AN OBELISK FLINC

Le Chiffre

I (and probably you) fancy myself to be a sort of real-life James Bond at times. What with my dapper style, cool composure, and action-packed life as a secret agent who takes down evildoers while casually sipping a drink that's been shaken, not stirred.

So I'm speaking from experience when I say one of the most compelling Bond villains of all time is Le Chiffre, financier to terrorist organizations the world over who attempts to best Bond in a poker game in *Casino Royale*. I've come across one or two Le Chiffre-like foes during my time in the field (and as a result have gotten quite good at poker). Like the character in the film, my own personal Le Chiffres are always quite indecipherable people, but I'm never at a loss for figuring them out.

If you haven't seen the movie, here's a relatively spoiler-free rundown—Le Chiffre loses a ton of money given to him by a terrorist. To save himself, he enters into a high stakes Texas Holdem tournament in a swanky Montenegro casino to win the money back. Bond is sent in to win the tournament and bankrupt Le Chiffre. Chaos and fabulousness ensue.

Holdem may seem like a risky way to settle matters of international importance. But there is a method to the madness. The key to a clean win, of course, is knowing what type of hand you have. But in some of those ultra-high-stakes games where people's lives are on the line, I can't just rely on the luck of the draw. My fellow undercover agents work the room, trying to catch a glimpse of my opponents' cards, then relay messages to me about the hand—be it tapped out in morse code on the rim of a martini glass or slipped to me on a cocktail napkin under my martini. (Did I mention I like martinis?)

But even having someone give you the low-down on your opponent's hand doesn't guarantee a win. You still have to keep your cool, bet smartly, and make the right decisions. I mean, if you were in a high stakes game and your evil opponent just went all in, what would you do? Call or fold?

This is today,
M

Hints: 105 • **Solution:** 148 • **Forum:** theorems.help/chiffre

YYYZMGJSH
JMLYKEOWI
SIQSLOLLW

Worth a Thousand Words

When the world gets too much and I need time in the cool, dark quiet to center my mind, I like to retreat to my personal rare book library. Imagine my climate controlled basement, a worn leather-bound book propped up in a cradle, me pouring over the yellowed parchment as delicate as spun sugar. What a salve to my occasionally frenzied mind!

Being a self-described bookworm, you already know I have a deep appreciation for books and the words contained within. And in many of these rare books the words are as beautiful as the illustrations that accompany them. The Gutenberg bible and its bold calligraphy, the history oozing from every curl in the Declaration of Independence's script, the stamp-like text of Poe's *Tamerlane and Other Poems*. But my crown jewel is the Voynich.

What is the Voynich, you ask? Only the most wonderfully bizarre rare book out there. Named for the rare books dealer who rediscovered it in the early 1900s, the codex dates back to the 1400s. It's page after undecipherable page of hand-written text in an unknown language accompanied by images of unidentifiable plants and mysterious cosmological diagrams.

Cryptographers have studied the version housed at Yale's rare book library for decades, certain that something in the relationship between the strange images and nonsensical script must hold some encoded secrets. But no one has been able to crack it. Little do they know, they haven't been studying the original. I managed to get a hold of that some time ago and swapped it out for a very convincing replica (but that's a story for another day).

And by George, I think I've got it figured out. It's like I was getting at before—you can't assume the words in a book are only a means to the story's end, simply there to build up a picture. Sometimes it's just the opposite.

This is today,

M

Jobbra

Ograhh

Dolaff

Prokki

Ugaarl

Llobid

Oongla

Eddric

Iggrun

A Modern Maker

Picture this: you're sitting for hours working out the design for a motion-tracking rubber band gun in your head. You did it. Solved. But now you've got to go through the drudgery of actually measuring and cutting and hammering. Feels like you've already done that though, right?

Making stuff is the best. There's nothing more satisfying than having an idea for an invention or art piece, then having it in your hand a short time later. But what comes in between is what sets a modern maker apart.

Back in the day, "making" was all about getting down and dirty in a workshop. And sure, getting all your fingers stuck together with superglue is still fun on occasion. But nowadays, we like to work smarter, not harder.

Welcome to the wonderful world of digital fabrication.

Today, there's all these automated tools that take in computer models and produce actual objects—all while you sip your coffee. Need some precise wooden gears? Laser cutter. Making an intricate engine part? A 5-axis CNC milling machine will do the trick. I've got them all in my J.A.R.V.I.S-inspired workshop, but of course my favorite is the humble 3D printer. By building up layer upon layer of material, these babies can make any object from pink plastic earrings to Martian habitats.

I do get that some people still love the feel of hammer in hand, though. That's why my latest project is using my room-size 3D printer to create an enormous steel sculpture—an ode to those old methods of making. When it's done, it'll stand proud in my personal sculpture garden for years to come, a tribute to the gone but not forgotten (if you get the point).

This is today,
M

D view

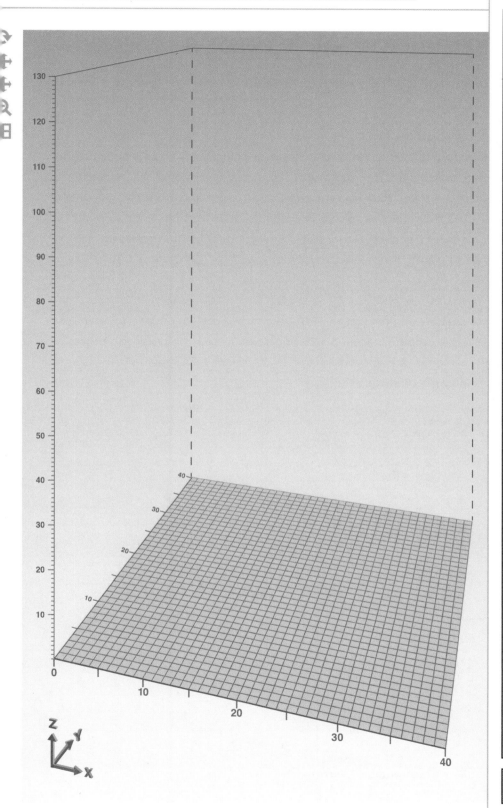

```
% an ode to the old
G28
G90
G20
G92 E0
M109 S1400 T0
M106 S255
G0 X18 Y36 Z0
G2 I0 J-18 E11
G1 Z2 E0.25 F15
G0 X36 Y18 Z0
G1 Z2 E0.5 F15
G0 X18 Y0 Z0
G1 Z2 E0.75 F15
G0 X0 Y18 Z0
G1 Z2 E1 F15
G2 I18 J0 E12
G1 X12 E13.1 F15
G0 X18 Y36
G1 Y24 E14.2 F15
G0 X36 Y18
G1 X24 E15.3 F15
G0 X18 Y0
G1 Y12 E16.4 F15
G2 I0 J6 E23.8
G1 Z110 E26.9 F15
G0 X12 Y18 Z2
G1 Z110 E37.4 F15
G0 X18 Y24 Z2
G1 Z110 E47.9 F15
G0 X24 Y18 Z2
G1 Z110 E58.4 F15
G1 X18 Y18 Z120 E59.5 F15
G1 Y12 Z110 E60.6 F15
G0 X12 Y18
G1 X18 Y18 Z120 E61.7 F15
G1 Y24 Z110 E62.8 F15
G0 X0 Y0 Z0
M104 S0 T0
M106 S0
%
```

Generate Model

Speaking of Vikings

The Vikings have a long history of being awesome. Sure they ransacked and pillaged to their hearts' content for hundreds of years. But they did more than that: they were the first documented Europeans to travel to North America. They had state-of-the-art ships and incredible navigation technologies for the time. And their gods were so awe-inspiring, they inspired the names for our days of the week. Looking to get married? Honor Frigg, the goddess of marriage, and do it on Frigg's Day (or Friday to us English folk). Feeling particularly warlike? Do battle on Tyr's Day (or Tuesday).

Just imagine being back there between the 9th and 11th centuries. Close your eyes and listen. That lilting Norweigian language resounding from intimidating ships as they rush ashore. Those Old Norse battle cries as braided Vikings ransack your village. By thunder! I'd be shaking in my lace-up boots. Cue Led Zeppelin to play me off to Valhalla.

This is today,

M

The Great Bacon Bake Off

I take my responsibility as a role model to the younger generation very seriously. I understand how important it is to cultivate curious minds, foster an interest in how the world works, and help them curate good taste. This last point is why, whenever anyone I know has a new baby, I get the kid a stuffed bacon. You squeeze it and it says "I'm Bacon." It's great.

Honestly, though, forget ambrosia. If there ever was an official food of the gods, bacon would be it. It pairs with anything—maple syrup, pasta, scallops, chocolate. It can be found around the world, from Italy to Brazil to Australia. And there's all sorts of types, too—American bacon of course, but also Back bacon, German Speck, the list goes on and on. Some have said my unique method of breakfast prep is a little pretentious, considering my choice of bacon. But they swallow those words when they take their first salty, fatty bite.

This is today,
M

American Bacon

Back Bacon

Faithless Finance

I've got a lot going on in my life. Between the last minute "business trips", regular astronomical observations, and revolving door of inventions in my home lab, I don't have a ton of time (or if we're being honest, the interest) to be bothered with the tedium of my finances.

That's why I have Q.

When I need to know if I have the funds for a room-sized 3D printer (I did) or capital to invest in a start-up to get humans to Mars (I will—soon), I turn to Q, my accountant and an industry veteran. He's the real deal, complete with eye shades, calculator, and plastic pocket protector.

Now, Q's got more integrity in just one of his mechanical pencils than most folks have combined. But from the original Ponzi scheme in the 1920s, to Bernie Madoff's variation on the theme nearly 90 years later, the financial sector is no stranger to scandal.

Q knows the struggle first hand. He once shared an anecdote with me about a company he felt compelled to report to the SEC. It was a puzzling organization not much unlike The Master Theorem, but one that had taken a serious turn to the dark side. Fascinated, I asked Q how many financial scandals there have been in total. With an arch look over his bifocals and the cynical tone only an accountant could muster, he replied, "In total? The answer, my friend, would shake your faith in humanity."

This is today,

M

The Sinister Theorem, LLC. Balance Sheet *(all values in millions)*

Assets

Current Assets:	
Cash (Earned & Stolen)	118
Petty Cash (Very Petty)	57
Supplies For Nefarious Missions	15
Accounts and Loans Receivable	309
Allowance for Losses from Shady Accounts	(72)
Inventory of Unsolvable Puzzles	43
Total Current Assets	475
Intangible Assets:	
Goodwill	3,820
Less Badwill	(3,173)
Trained Henchmen	556
Loyal (Unsuspecting?) Customers	871
Labyrinthian Warehouse ("Acquired")	28
Total Intangible Assets	2,111
TOTAL ASSETS	2,579

Liabilities & Stockholder's Equity

Liabilities:	
Current Liabilities:	
Loans and Mortgage Payable, Due Within 1 Year	892
Allowance for Lack of Desire to Pay	(454)
Accounts Payable	13
Allowance for Lack of Desire to Pay	(6)
Accrued Interest Payable	77
Allowance for Lack of Desire to Pay	(20)
Low Wages Payable	382
Total Current Liabilities	892
Long Term Liabilities:	
Loans Payable, Due After 1 Year	121
Mortgage Payable on Warehouse, Due After 1 Year	7
Allowance for Plan to Skip Town	(61)
Total Long Term Liabilities	87
Total Liabilities	956
Stockholder's Equity:	
Founder's (Highly) Preferred Stock	612
Common(er's) Stock	50
Additional Paid-in-Capital	401
Retained Earnings	558
Total Stockholder's Equity	1,626
TOTAL LIABILITIES AND STOCKHOLDER'S EQUITY	2,586

Dreaming in Dimensions

As you've seen in my first book, I'm pretty interested in documenting how my brain works. I've delved into my synaesthesia and the strange utterings that echo in my brain as I'm falling asleep. Today I want to tell you a little bit about what happens when I finally arrive in dreamland.

It probably won't surprise you to know I have incredibly vivid dreams—with epic storylines. Usually I'm saving the world from terrorists or climate change, or jumping around through time like it's NBD. My dreams are too cool to forget, so I like to record them in whatever way makes sense. Sometimes I write them down. Sometimes I draw or chart them.

In one particularly poignant dream, I was walking down an abandoned city street lined with quaint shops lit only by the shine of the moon. As I strolled, I approached a lone street light that illuminated a sign which read, "Caution: You are approaching the intersection of four dimensions." A real Twilight Zone kind of vibe.

The sign listed an address of a nearby brownstone apartment. I walked to the apartment, and let myself in. As soon as I entered, three other ghostly versions of me split from my being and fanned out into the room. Each of me came from an alternate dimension, and we quickly fell into casual conversation about our lives. They were all very similar but slightly different because we all made slightly different choices in life.

I love my life, and parts of my timeline were certainly better, but I was a little jealous of parts of theirs, too. I wished I could be a cross dimensional being, look up into those other dimensions, and pick and choose different features to create my own perfect, custom timeline.

So with enormous hubris, I forced my way into those other timelines like a character from *Dark Matter* to steal what I wanted. But I'm distubed to report that my custom timeline didn't turn out to be the personal utopia I was hoping for. My dream-self should have remembered all those warnings from dystopian sci-fi movies: trying to control your own fate like that typically backfires.

This is today,
M

Hints: 108 • **Solution:** 160 • **Forum:** theorems.help/dimensions

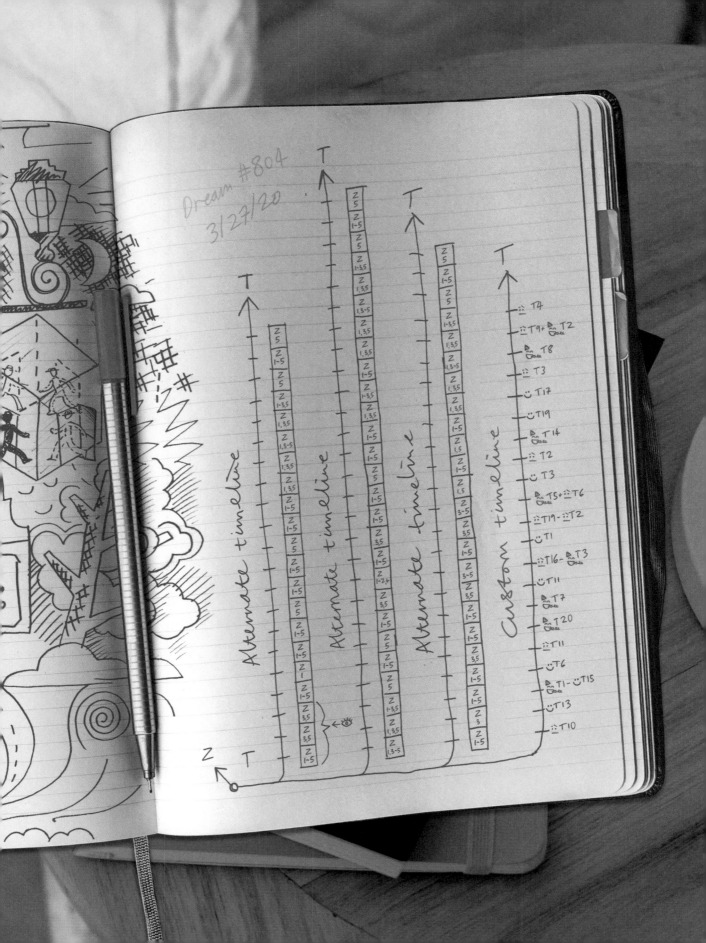

A Colossal Colonnade

There's a lasting elegance to the art of architecture. Buildings from centuries ago still stand today, giving us a history of world progress—from temples in Malta to Dr. Seuss-esque modernist museums, from Mayan cities to the skyline of Hong Kong.

It's not just buildings that stand the test of time, either. Techniques invented way back in ancient Greece or Rome still make appearances in the architecture of today. Arches, domes, mosaic floors, decorative relief. Or take the different orders of classical columns, for instance. They started off humble, simply a way to brace facets of a building. But they've branched out in style over the centuries, from simple fluting to ornate florals. And now, take a drive through any city, suburb, or small town in the world and odds are, you'll find variations on these orders of classical columns adorning houses, bridges, municipal buildings, and more.

Makes sense, though. When something exists for that long, it must be doing something right. Why mess with a classic?

This is today,
M

Hints: 108 • **Solution:** 162 • **Forum:** theorems.help/colonnade

SDR4HXOH4I0ELEO2CXVASEASAPTSRX

AIRILXTNCIAUCROHOSSOCTCNUD&NNM

WLHETTNCNIEIOTYAIEINWDFEEHOESR

The ABCs of E.T.'s DNA

Some people might view *Jurassic Park* as a cautionary tale. I just see it as a challenge. Which is why I'm all set up like a benevolent version of The InGen Corporation with a decked out biohacking lab in my basement.

With some sensors, controls, tubes, and chemicals I can do complex DNA replication experiments from the comfort of my own home. My recent partnership with NASA's SETI Institute means I've mostly been using this tech to model what alien DNA—and, by extension, aliens themselves—might look like. I've got a real Spielberg kind of vibe going on. *Jurassic Park* meets *E.T.*, if you will.

Just imagine all those twisty double helixes, chock full of adenines, thymines, cytosines, and guanines, paired up and strung together in specific patterns that code for the traits of any given organism on Earth—from hair color to scaliness.

But there are a whole bunch of different environments across the universe that life could evolve in, leading to vastly different organic chemistries and complex patterns in their unfamiliar DNA base pairs. Some life forms might use different elements—like silicon instead of carbon, or arsenic instead of phosphorus. Water worlds, microgravity, methane rain—any of these could cause our alien friends to evolve with unique genes that express quite remarkable physical traits.

And we know from studying all the different organisms here on Earth that if there's a niche to fill, some crazy form of life will fill it. In fact, there's plenty of alien-looking life right here on our own planet. As they say, "Life...uh...finds a way."

This is today,

M

Hints: 108 • **Solution:** 164 • **Forum:** theorems.help/dna

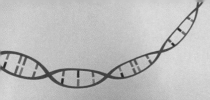

TRAIT 1: OILY SCALES   TRAIT 2: PURPLE SKIN   TRAIT 3: FOUR EYES   TRAIT 4: POISON SALIVA

```
O N D I L Q Y K S C P B R K L G S N I O E N F A Q H D T A M F R A F G K H G I M
X A I G I L K E W S K U Q P X E V K A N D B X E D R G C O B C A N H L P D B M N
```

TRAIT 1: SMOOTH SHELL   TRAIT 2: PINK SPIKES   TRAIT 3: SEVEN ANTENNAE   TRAIT 4: AIR SAC

```
A S P R M W O O P T S P D N T S F I C E M M J B I U M F G D A L S M W A K R U B
H V S B H E O J L S L L I P K I P E K H S E M D D C K Z M D R Z H D D H G A F A
```

TRAIT 1: FLUFFY EARS   TRAIT 2: GREEN FUR   TRAIT 3: FIVE LEGS   TRAIT 4: GLOWING STRIPES

```
K U F L Y U K D F B G M E A N D U K U D K H D H F A D F H V C K C O A D F C A I
F T Y D E A N R E S G R S E S F M R C D E B F R G E C F G A F C D D S N C M D J
```

TRAIT 1: ???   TRAIT 2: ???   TRAIT 3: ???   TRAIT 4: ???

```
Y T S Q H K A Q R B X U W B C O E D E G C H Q G D R G S A I Q A F A N C A S O C
P B E G J A D K X R L R E P L P O B D F Q Z I B D K D J S J D B N H A K B B A P
```

— — — — — — —

Frittering Away

Pool is cool. And don't just take my word for it. Just watch Paul Newman, Jackie Gleason, and the rest of the cast of the 1961 classic *The Hustler* knock their way around a pool table and you'll see what I mean. The smoke-filled hall, the clacking of the balls as another color disappears into a pocket. That film brought pool to the danger level of "asking for a favor on this the day of my daughter's wedding."

Still, I can't say I'm entirely sure why a game that requires a nerdy level of math and physics has been co-opted by the rough and tumble crowd. I suppose it could also partly be Hugh Jackman's fault, with his Broadway role as the protector from pool hall debaucheries, saving youngsters from that grimy, gritty institution that acts as a gateway to the darker side of life. Adamantium claws or no, his whole tough guy persona really fits right at home in those mischievous pool halls.

This is today,
M

Hints: 109 • **Solution:** 166 • **Forum:** theorems.help/pool

A Smart Move

People talk about mastery of strategy games like Chess, Checkers, and Go as being the hallmarks of a genius mind. But I argue that the true genius mind is the one that can build a mind that never loses such games. I'm talking, of course, about programmers who make world-champion-defeating artificial intelligences.

I have been a competitive Checkers enthusiast for decades, now. I'm internationally ranked and have even gotten close to beating the best AI opponent the world has to offer. But then I realized—why settle for second best? Why not create a Checkers AI to end all Checkers AIs?

And so, I developed the equivalent of Deep Blue to Garry Kasparov, the AlphaGo to Ke Jie.

After refining it with my cryptographer buddies, I installed it on some custom-built, WiFi-connected boards and sent it to Checkers masters around the world. That way, when they play against my AI, I can track how badly they lose move by move.

I call the whole set up CheckMark, because that's what I put next to each name of a Checkers master that my AI destroys in the game.

Long live CheckMark!

This is today,
M

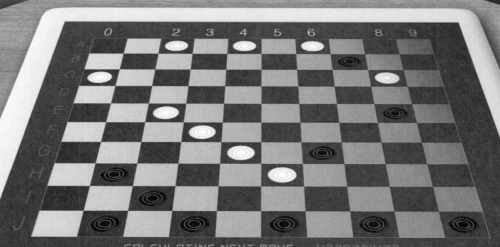

How I Wonder Who You Are

When you're first published, everyone tells you not to look at your reviews. If they're good, they say, that's nice. But if they're bad, they're soul crushing.

I followed this advice for a little while when my first murder mystery came out. But I write about debonair detectives and their clever sleuthing of inscrutable mysteries for the love of the craft, not because I require any sort of external validation. And no way was I going to pass up the chance to see what anonymous randos were saying about me on the internet!

Despite a few hilariously negative reviews, turns out I was one of the lucky ones. Here's a sampling of my favorites.

★ ★ ★ ★ ★ Sadie F.
"...M's writing is incandescent..."

★ ★ ★ ★ ★ Miles C.
"...a rising star in the murder mystery scene..."

★ ★ ★ ★ ★ Priya R.
"...the word choice and turns of phrase are just heavenly..."

★ ☆ ☆ ☆ ☆ Mark P.
"dumb"

Hey, good or bad, people were talking about my work. And that was just the kind of boost I needed to light my path through the darkest night to write another novel.

This is today,
M

Hints: 110 • **Solution:** 170 • **Forum:** theorems.help/wonder

The coastal Maine village of Celeste was shrouded in the colors of a midsummer sunset. The brightest stars had just begun to twinkle above the park as the sky slowly darkened. It had been a peaceful day in this sleepy Greek neighborhood, but for the seven sisters that renowned detective Virginia Gomez was about to question, this had been anything but a peaceful year.

Gomez—methodical, analytical, and ever with an eye for detail—took in the scene. The eldest, Maya, led her sisters in a meditative pilates session to calm their nerves. Even in these trying times, the socialites sparkled under the moonlight, though one of them was hard to spot in the increasing darkness. Their bodyguard, Tau, a stable and reliable man built like a bull, circled the sisters protectively. They situated themselves near the banks of a great river that flowed right out into the sea. In the park for just a few minutes, Gomez noticed the sea was teeming with life—fish, a whale, a dolphin, even a goat swam by. She took some photos with her telescopic camera lens to file away with other evidence.

Tau grunted a warning as Gomez approached, but Maya waved him off. "You again? I thought we already answered all of your questions," she huffed as her sister Elle unfolded herself from a complex position.

The no-nonsense detective ignored her. "As you know, your neighbor Ori was murdered last winter, found laying upside down in the outback of Australia after a hunting trip, his two dogs still by his side. And this summer, not too long after Ori disappeared, your friend Scott Prius was found murdered with an arrow through his chest. We believe this can all be traced back to that infamous house party you hosted last winter. I need you to tell me more about it."

Tay lit up with frustration. "Look, we've been through this. There were 88 people on the invite list, but it must have been Mercury in Retrograde or something. It was foggy that night—people had trouble getting there through the milky haze."

Cela seamlessly continued, "Yeah, the only ones who showed were Tau, Ori and one of his dogs, the twins who live just east of us. Scott, of course. Oh and our good friend Cass, sporting a shirt with her startup's trademark W-shaped logo."

"Can you remember if anyone else was also there?" Gomez asked.

Ali chimed in with a twinkle in her eye. "Oh! There was this weird-looking, horse-faced guy, too. Apparently he's super independent—always traveling—which is why he never came to one of our parties before."

Mer, the youngest, beamed, "I think I heard someone calling him SGR!"

"Interesting. Did anything else happen that night?" Gomez asked.

Stera took over. "Well, Ori was hitting on all of us like usual. But he started to get out of hand. Tau was keeping a watchful eye on Ori, but even so, Scott is an assertive guy and gave Ori a piece of his mind. Whatever he said must have stung. I don't think they've spoken or even been in the same place together since.

"It more than stung. Scott killed Ori," Gomez dropped to the group's gasps. "But now, who killed Scott? Someone who wanted vengeance for Ori's death. Someone physically close to Scott."

A distant bell chimed 1900 hours. A gust of seawind chilled the air, like the temperature had suddenly plunged to -25 degrees. Gomez's walkie talkie screeched with a strong, piercingly loud radio signal. Out of nowhere, a beast-like man with a bow and arrow lunged out of the bushes towards the sisters. Before any damage could be done, ever-watchful Tau tackled him to the ground.

"Looks like my hunch was right." Gomez said. "This 'weird-looking' guest of yours will be trotting right to jail. The scales of justice are up there with Scott tonight."

The sisters sighed, remembering the friends they lost. "What consolation is that anyway?"

I Can Has Obscure Book?

I was just about work on this Theorem when I got a call from a blocked number on my burner phone. We all know what that means.

A crime boss I'd been tracking turned up in a small town on the edge of the Black Forest in Germany. So off I went, but by the time I got there, he'd vanished into that fabled wood from Brothers Grimm lore. All I could find were some innocuous trail signs detailing the different inspirations for those rather dark fairy tales. A cute tourist attraction, I thought, but nothing that would help me find my villain.

But while perusing the local library that evening, I came across an early edition of *Steganographia* by the self-proclaimed "most revered and famous man, Johannes Trithemius, Abbot of Sponheim, & Most Perfect Master of Natural Magic." (I kid you not, that's how he credited himself. And you thought I could be over-the-top sometimes.)

Steganography is the name for all the sneaky ways one can send a message without having to encrypt it. The idea, in contrast, is that you can just hide the message so no one suspects it's there unless they know to look for it. Think invisible ink, notes underneath postage stamps, Morse code in knots on yarn woven into someone's clothing, or carefully tweaked color information in a photo's pixels.

The most revered and famous Trithemius is the first known to have used the term in his series of three books that make up *Steganographia*. To regular browsers at the 17th century bookshop, it read like a manual on how to use spirits and angels to transmit messages. But the initiated knew to use a separately published decryption key, and found a treatise on cryptography. Quite contrasting subject matters!

This all got me wondering if there wasn't more to those Black Forest signs than first met the eye. On a hunch, I returned that night with a black light and found each sign held a fluorescent arrow pointing me to my long sought-after bad guy.

Needless to say, after the excitement of my mission, I was too tired to finish this Theorem. So, as a contrast to your normal puzzling routine, please enjoy this picture of a cat instead.

This is today,
M

Hints: 110 • **Solution:** 172 • **Forum:** theorems.help/cat

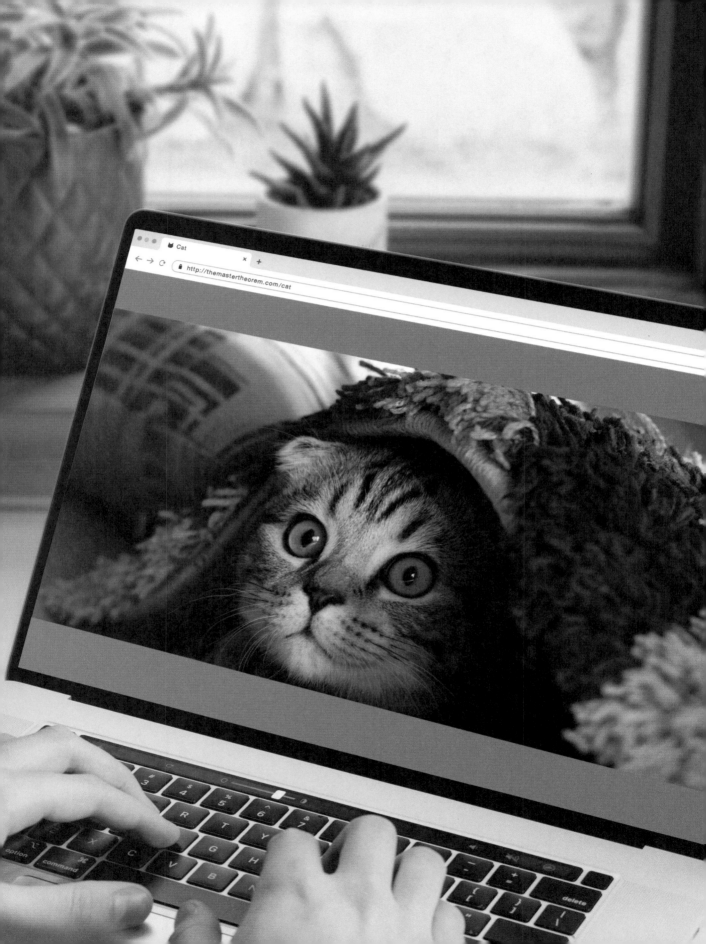

My Bread and Butter

Cooking is so much more than combining ingredients to arrive at edible sustenance. What we prepare in the kitchen, and how we prepare it, is like a window into ourselves. You know what they say: some people make cheese omelets, and others make rosemary-smoked quail eggs served over a bed of bubbling dry ice.

Me? True to form, I'm of the more scientific mindset when I'm at the stovetop. Armed with my ultra-precise kitchen scale and a suite of measuring cups (SI units only, of course), I approach each recipe with the same precision I use in my DNA lab.

And as with any experiment, there's plenty of room for creativity. That's why I often turn to my trusty *Flavor Bible* to figure out exactly what ingredients go well together. If I need to know what I could combine with, say, jicama, I flip to its entry in that trusty resource to find I should try chile powder and lime juice. And then I tinker until I find the relative quantities that will make each flavor pop.

But the most important ingredients to add to your cooking? Love and personality, of course.

What, too cliché?

This is today,
M

Hints: 110 • **Solution:** 174 • **Forum:** theorems.help/cooking

The Crown Jewels of Colouring

I bet you've been feeling stressed from all this puzzling. I know just what you need.

See, I often find myself in high stress situations, too. Whether shimmying along the windows of a high rise in Dubai, attempting to best Garry Kasparov in chess, or frantically triple-checking my calculations to be absolutely sure my new particle accelerator won't create a singularity that consumes us all, life just keeps upping the stakes, amirite?

So when I finally get home, I like to break out my coloring books. There's something about the sight of those beautiful patchworks of color that just soothes my nervous system. To me, a good coloring session is akin to meditating in a sensory deprivation chamber.

There's been a glorious resurgence in adult coloring books over the past few years, too. You've got nature themes, space themes, ocean themes. Coloring books with extra doodling options, those with swear words in elegant swirls, even the color-by-number types so you don't have to make any difficult decisions yourself. Really, if coloring is your jam, you'll find a book to match your stress-reduction needs.

No matter which version you choose, completing a coloring page makes you feel like you deserve a spot in the Tate Modern. So, here you go—relax, enjoy. When you're done, take a step back, marvel at your work, and be proud of what you've created.

Then go take a 14 hour nap. After all these Theorems, you (and I) deserve it.

This is today,

M

Foraging 101

It's always handy to know which plants you can and can't eat. When you're deep in the jungle without supplies because you're hot on the trail of a hidden terrorist sect, you gotta go with what the land gives you.

Humans have understood that since... well, almost forever. Way back (and back and back and back) in the day, our hunter-gatherer ancestors did all the heavy lifting and figured out which berries and leaves were delicious or medicinal, and which would bring on a slow and agonizing death. (Don't think too hard about *how* they figured this out. Just be grateful that enough of them chose correctly.)

So today, I pass this ancient knowledge on to you. Whether you're hunting terrorists in the wilderness or just out for a stroll in your city park, here are a few of the more valuable tips I've learned during my foraging escapades.

- First and foremost, always keep a foraging journal to track the plants and landscapes you've encountered.
- Avoid only knowing plants by their common names. Trust me, you wouldn't want to accidentally make some hemlock tea with poison hemlock (*Conium maculatum*) instead of clippings from the eastern hemlock tree (*Tsuga canadensis*).
- Over-harvesting hurts the natural balance of the landscape. Keep track of how many plants you gather to make sure you aren't picking more than you can eat.
- If you're foraging at home, try an app like PlantNet to more easily identify what you encounter. But remember, in a real survival situation you need to know this stuff like the back of your hand.

Happy foraging!

This is today,
M

The Minor Theorem

So, I like math. When you apply it correctly, the limit of what it can help you do is infinite. Calculus has been integral in my work with rocket trajectories. Linear algebra was a guiding vector in developing the inverse kinematics for my robotic arm. And discrete math has let me (discreetly) prove that P does in fact equal NP.

But I do understand that some of you out there in the world are not the biggest fans of math. And I get it. If you don't know what you're looking at, it can be really overwhelming. All those Greek symbols just make math feel like, well, Greek to some people.

But when you get down to it, math isn't really so scary. It's a methodical undertaking. As long as you have something to reference that will help you wade through those symbols, you can just take it all step by step.

And once you get into it, it can open up the world to you. As a wise junior at North Shore High once said, "I like math...because it's the same in every country."

Truer words were never spoken.

This is today,
M

Hints: 111 • **Solution:** 180 • **Forum:** theorems.help/math

THE MINOR THEOREM

GIVEN THESE AXIOMS:

η is any positive whole number

θ is a chain of X numbers written as $\eta_1 :: \eta_2 :: \ldots :: \eta_X$

Σ is a series of Y chains written as $\theta_1 >> \theta_2 >> \ldots >> \theta_Y$

$\eta_{a,\beta}$ is the ath number in the βth chain in Σ

$\delta(\eta)$ is the remainder of $\eta/26$

$\lambda(\eta)$ is the ηth letter of the alphabet when $\eta \leq 26$, or the $\delta(\eta)^{th}$ letter when $\eta > 26$

$\omega(\theta)$ is the word represented by chain θ

$\mu(\omega)$ is the numeric value of a number written out as word ω

IT FOLLOWS THAT:

For any Σ :

$$\omega(\theta_1) = \lambda(\eta_{1,1})\,\lambda(\eta_{2,1})\ldots\lambda(\eta_{X,1})$$

and for all β where $2 \leq \beta \leq Y$:

$$\omega(\theta_\beta) = \lambda(\eta_{1,\beta} + \mu(\omega(\theta_{\beta-1})))\,\lambda(\eta_{2,\beta} + \mu(\omega(\theta_{\beta-1})))\ldots\lambda(\eta_{X,\beta} + \mu(\omega(\theta_{\beta-1})))$$

AND AS A COROLLARY:

$$Q = \lambda(\mu(\omega(\theta_1)))\,\lambda(\mu(\omega(\theta_2)))\ldots\lambda(\mu(\omega(\theta_Y)))$$

PROBLEM #1
Using The Minor Theorem solve for Q :

20::23::5::12::22::5 >> 20::23::10::19 >> 15::3::4::13::15::26::26::9 >>
7::21::22::5::7::18::18::1 >> 2::1::18

In the Eye of the Beholder

If you're looking for something to add to your bucket list, I've got just the thing: Go visit the Uffizi Gallery in Florence, Italy on a warm November day. The tourist season is over by then, so it'll be just you, the locals, and the paintings.

Ah, those paintings.

I love wandering those rambling halls, watching art history magically unfold before my eyes in room after room of masterworks dating as far back as the early 1200s.

The paintings that really capture my imagination, though, are those of the Renaissance artists. Call me a traditionalist, but works like Botticelli's *Birth of Venus*, Michaelangelo's *Sistine Chapel*, and Raphael's *School of Athens* are among the best ever produced. These Da Vinci-day Da Vincis managed to capture scenes with the depth and richness of photographs thanks to innovations in using geometry and color theory to create realistic tableaux.

Each Renaissance master had an eye for even the minutest details that magically transformed paint on paper into a living, breathing scene. Look at their paintings the right way, and you'd swear the subjects were popping out of the frames right before your eyes.

This is today,
M

Hints: 112 • **Solution:** 182 • **Forum:** theorems.help/art

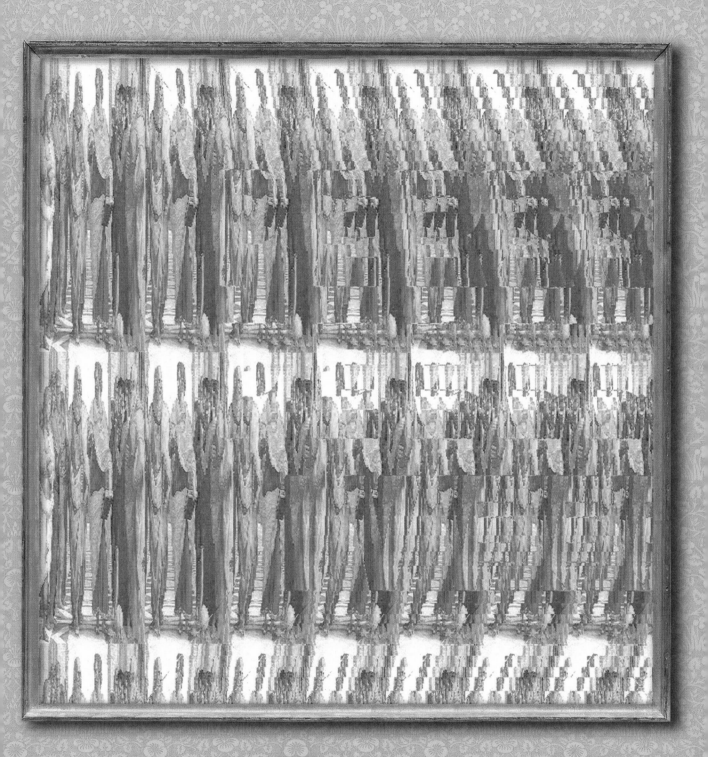

The School of Athens
by Raphael
(a digital reproduction)

Grandpre, Je t'aime

For me and my cryptographer buddies, the sporting event par excellence is not the Superbowl, not the World Series, not even the World Cup. It's the Monaco Grandpre. Those incredible high tech cars whipping around tight corners, zipping past spectators on yachts, howling through a dark tunnel just inspire incalculable awe.

It's apt that Monaco is home to one of the most prestigious races in the world. It's a mere 1,000 kilometers from where the first auto race was held in 1894. You can trace the historical path from that race to the first Grandpre in 1906, to the Formula One of today—that most superior of motorsports.

Not knocking NASCAR or anything—that's actually a pretty impressive race experience in its own right—but Grandpre racing takes the proverbial cake as far as the science of the sport. The cars are perfectly calibrated to exacting specifications. The crews are experts not only in mechanics and aerodynamics, but also computer science, using onboard sensors and data to optimize their cars for the next race. But the pièce de résistance? None of that tech can be used to improve a driver's performance when they're on the course—all that whipping and zipping and howling is done by human skill alone.

Mon dieu! Cars, tech, and sheer human grit all combined into one glamorous sport? What's not to love?

This is today,
M

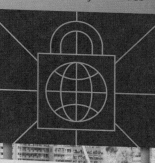
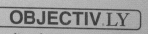

World-Wide Wanderings

I'm like the poster child for wanderlust. You'd think I'd get my fill, with all my jet setting. But during my down time, after I've 3D printed and written murder mysteries and manipulated DNA to my heart's content, I like to satisfy any residual ennui by taking to the great outdoors.

Wandering down leaf-strewn paths, rowing along narrow creeks, keeping my eyes and ears peeled for a hint of wildlife—all of this poetically reminds me that if you can just get off the beaten path, there's so much out there to experience.

Of course, like any modern human, I like to share my trips and resultant musings with the world on Instagram. I take photos at every step along the way with the hopes of inspiring others to head to the hiking trails on their next day off.

But maybe they should bring a park ranger-sanctioned map. Mine might be a little too haphazard to follow.

This is today,
M

Dreamland Textures

I've said it before and I'll say it again: Brains are weird. Take mine, for example. Between my synaesthetic association of letters with colors and my dreams about alternate dimensions, you never know what this crazy bundle of electrical firings is going to come up with next.

So, I'm here to share with you yet another bizarre entry in my attempts to document my brain. For as long as I can remember, smells, tastes—even emotions—forcefully bring to mind various textures. Fresh cut grass smells spikey. Watermelon tastes fluffy. Happiness is distinctly glossy.

It's related to my synesthesia, I'm sure, but it's much more prominent when I'm on the edge of dreams. As I fall asleep, (in addition to hearing the poetic mutterings of nonsensical phrases) vivid textures regularly flash before my eyes. Pink fur. Spiky metal. Smooth wood.

Much like how my dreams help me process my waking hours, these textures seem to represent my mindset at the time. If I focus on the textures for long enough, I bring the subconscious to the fore and can see what they're trying to tell me. The coarser the texture, the more anxious I am. If they're smooth and soft, I know I'm in a good headspace.

It makes me wonder: if I took everything that's happened in my life, every emotion I've ever felt, all the awesome stuff I've done and heard and even eaten, what texture would represent the totality of me?

This is today,
M

Of Thee I Sing

I love America.

Don't worry—it's not in, like, a 'Murica way. I recognize that there are flaws in our country and political system (oh boy, are there flaws...), but still I'm proud of who we are and I've proudly fought to defend our freedoms. As we've proven time and again, Americans will not be kept down. As a people, we are so beautifully diverse, but we can truly unite when we need to.

So that's why the Fourth of July is my favorite holiday. What better way to celebrate this melting pot than to gather with a motley crew of friends, throw some burgers, hot dogs, and corn on the cob on the grille, and turn up my playlist filled with America-themed tunes.

Just gotta make sure I don't get so distracted by patriotic fervor that I forget to turn what's on the grille.

This is today,
M

July 4th Playlist

G	Y	B	I	'	E
R	G	U	O	T	K
M	K	P	L	N	E
Y	O	H	W	A	Y
I	A	I	H	'	D
M	'	S	M	O	Y
U	T	O	N	E	N
O	A	A	H	Y	G
			N	P	E
				N	S

Monstrous Math

As you know from our previous outings with Snippets and Proof!, the gaming wing of this whole operation—a branding front for The Master Theorem known as Evermade—is a powerhouse of neuron-challenging fun. But if I had my way, these games would be hard enough to rival even the Mensa admission test.

Take our newest mathematical offering, Adsumudi (cleverly named for ADdition, SUbtraction, MUltiplication, and DIvision). In this game, you have a card with a target number in the center and five numbers surrounding it. Depending on the difficulty level, you need to use between two and five of the surrounding numbers to make an equation that equals the target in the middle. First to come up with a solution using the four namesake mathematical operations shouts "Adsumudi!" and wins the card. You can read up on it and test out your skills at **http://adsumudi.com**.

But in draft one, players had to deal with math a little more monstrous. Addition, subtraction, multiplication and division were banned and in their stead I demanded players only use sine (or inverse sine), modulus, exponent, and logarithm. You still got five numbers to use, but you had to use all of them and only once each. Oh, and there was no target. You had to figure that out (though still a positive whole number) on your own. Fun, right?

Just in case you're rusty on your high school trig and pre-calc, I've given you the rundown on those operations at **http://themastertheorem.com/math**. Seriously, go take a look.

Unfortunately, my marketing team had doubts that this game would get broad appeal, so they convinced me to scale back to present day Adsumudi. Too bad, I was looking forward to hearing shouts of the old name at game nights the world over.

This is today,
M

Hints: 114 • **Solution:** 192 • **Forum:** theorems.help/adsumudi

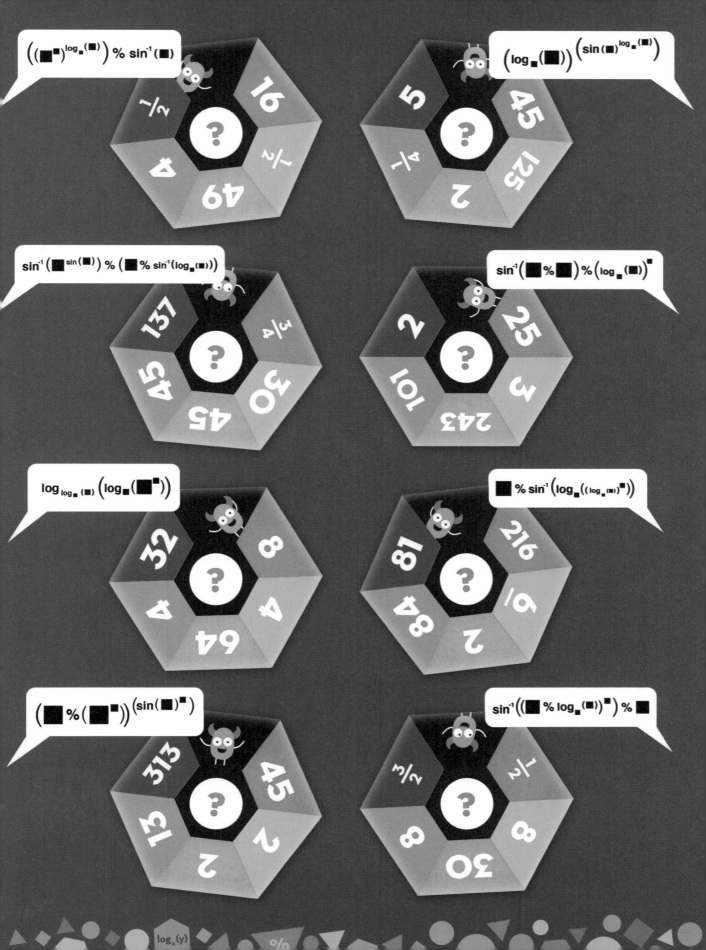

The Right to Write

Where would humanity be without words? About 6,500 languages are spoken in our world today with between 200 and 400 alphabets. All together that makes millions of those wonderful, little conceptual nuggets.

To quote the inimitable Mark Twain, "The difference between the almost right word and the right word is the difference between the lightning bug and the lightning." Meaning, of course, that the more you know about language the more you can articulate what's in your brain to the outside world. There are so many tricks of the trade, too: simile and metaphor, metonymy and synecdoche, homophones and onomatopoeia. The altogether effect being authors can affect the way people see the world.

You might ask, are our words truly that important? Edward Bulwer-Lytton said it best with his oft-repeated phrase, "the pen is mightier than the sword." Whether you're discussing something as mundane as the weather or as complex as your own personal philosophy, there's always specificity in the language chosen.

That's never more true than with authors. Sometimes they're so wrapped up in their word choice, there's trouble figuring out where their use of the language ends and they themselves begin.

This is today,
M

ROSE THEIR CARROT ___ FOR SEA KARAT T'S ROWS PRAISE BUY YOU ___ PRAYS TEAS '

___ TEASE MEDAL PREYS TWO ___ METAL CENTS PRAYS OUR CARET '

"

___ NOSE THERE CARAT RHOS THEY'RE KARAT YOUR ___ ONE BYE SEE ___ HOUR MEDDLE U

AISLE METTLE AFFECT CARET ___ NO'S BY YORE TO TEES ___ I'LL CARROT METAL EWE

TEASE BY ___ ISLE MEDAL YEW WON ___ TOO PRAISE WHICH WITCH CARROT YOU'RE KARAT U ROSE

"

___ ROES THERE PREYS YOU WHERE T'S ___ .

___

___ SCENTS CARAT KNOWS PRAYS TEAS ___ PRAISE YEW

___ RHOS THEIR YOUR BYE C WEAR THEY'RE ___ ROSE THERE KARAT

___

___ SENSE BUY BYE EFFECT PRAISE EWE WHERE ___ WARE CENTS MEDDLE TEAS TEASE

Einstein's Greatest Puzzle

Say you have twin astronauts—let's call them, oh I don't know, Mark and Scott Kelly. Mark blasts off to visit, say, Alpha Centauri at 75% the speed of light, while Scott stays put on Earth. From Scott's Earth-based perspective, Alpha Centauri is 4.4 light years away and he'll be waiting 11.7 years for his brother to return. But for Mark, who's traveling at ultra high speed, the distance to Alpha Centauri actually contracts to 2.9 light years and the round trip only takes 7.7 years. That means that upon Mark's return, Scott will be 4 years older than his identical twin brother.

Wild.

Einstein's incredible intellect knew not the bounds of time or space. When he came up with the Theory of Special Relativity back in 1905, the world was stunned by it's more out-there implications. Like how things moving at near-light speeds physically shorten—called length contraction—and experience time to stretch, or run more slowly—called time dilation.

And these effects aren't just relegated to nerdy thought experiments—the predictions Einstein made about a century ago are actually used in functional day-to-day ways.

Take GPS, for example. The satellites beaming down positioning signals are moving faster than us here on Earth so time is running slower for them, too. If we didn't compensate for that, our phones might place us in Miami when we were really in Boston. (Although, would that actually be so bad?)

All of this is why I still maintain that when Han says the Millennium Falcon did the Kessel Run in less than 12 parsecs, he didn't mistake parsec as a unit of time! He was, in fact, talking about relativistic length contraction (we're ignoring the existence of *Solo*. That's better for everyone).

So, a long time from now (or rather, a long, long time ago), when business trips to the moons of Neptune become the norm, calendar reminders better take these effects into account. Event Title? Got it. Event Date? Here you go. Speed at Which You Will Be Traveling to Event? Ugh.

This is today,
M

Hints: 115 • Solution: 196 • Forum: theorems.help/einstein

Outer Spice Inc.

Business Observational Log
August 8th, 2361

On this day, five Outer Spice Inc. ships left earth at relativistic speeds to collect exotic spices being grown on comets at the outer edges of the solar system. Each ship had a different name, traveled at a different fraction of the speed of light, and experienced a different amount of time dilation and length contraction.

- The ship that experienced an 8m length contraction also experienced a 2h time dilation.

- The Milky Caraway was traveling faster than The Seed of Light but slower than the ship that underwent an 8h time dilation.

- The ship that contracted in length by 15m was traveling at 50% the speed of light.

- The ship traveling at 70% the speed of light experienced a smaller length contraction than Parsley by the Parsec.

- The Seed of Light was traveling at 60% the speed of light.

- The ship that experienced a 15h time dilation experienced a length contraction greater than the ship that experienced a 5h time dilation.

- The Mintergalactic experienced a 4m length contraction.

- The ship traveling at 65% the speed of light experienced an 8m length contraction.

- Earth to Cardamom was traveling slower than the ship that experienced both a 6m length contraction and a 4h time dilation.

- The ship that experienced a 14m length contraction experienced a time dilation greater than the ship traveling at 55% the speed of light.

- Parsley by the Parsec experienced a time dilation of 4h.

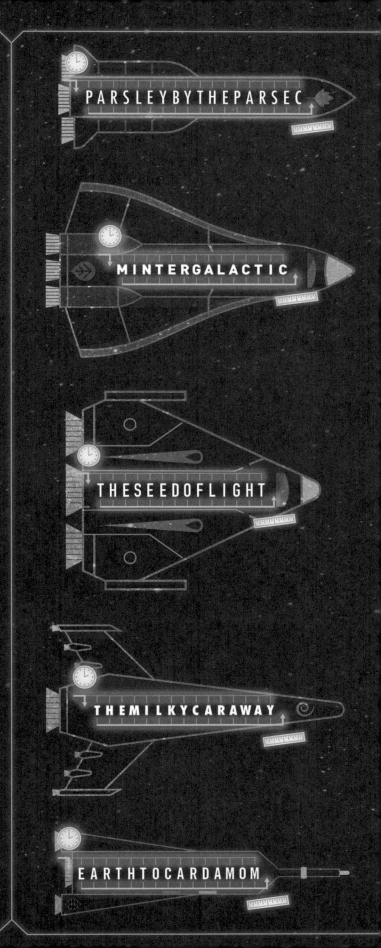

Aboriginal

I'd like to begin by acknowledging the traditional custodians of the land from which this Theorem originates.

As a post grad, I spent some time doing an ethnographic study in Australia not too far from Uluru, the awe-inspiring rock that juts out of the desert in the middle of the country. It's a sacred site for many Aboriginal, or indigenous, peoples, and I can understand why. The way its orange mass juts from the desert is awesome in the true sense of the word.

The local Anangu people have a beautiful, spiritual story about the rock's origin. In fact, the hundreds of separate Aboriginal nations from throughout the continent each have their own fascinating takes on how many things came to be, like the constellations in the night sky and their own ancestors. It was an enlightening journey to be able to live and learn there, absorbing these origin stories of nature while completely surrounded by it.

But the Aboriginal and Torres Strait Islander people of Australia, much like indigenous people the world over, have been historically forced from their homelands and subjected to terrible treatment—both by the original settlers and systemically since.

Luckily, things have gotten a little better in modern times. In 1985, the Australian government officially recognized the Anangu people as the traditional owners of the land around Uluru, leading the way for other indigenous people to regain their land rights as well. And more recently, it has become common practice to place respectful statements acknowledging the country's original occupants everywhere from websites to menus to movie previews (and even Theorems).

Still, spending time with these people made viscerally real to me the suffering and mistreatment they've endured for nearly 250 years. So I can understand why Australia Day, which celebrates the origin story of European settlers in the country, has been getting a critical reevaluation in recent years. Doesn't seem like something I'd want to celebrate either (looking at you, Columbus Day).

This is today,
M

Hints: 115 • Solution: 198 • Forum: theorems.help/aboriginal

Everyone Hates Moral Philosophy Professors

Like a certain fictional dead (then not dead, then dead again, then ~moved on~) moral philosopher, I tend to overthink matters of morals and ethics. But when you are regularly making life or death decisions in the course of saving the world, you're bound to run into some major moral quandaries. What gives me the right to make these decisions? Do I owe anyone restitution for the things I've done, in the interest of society though they were? Does anything we do really matter anyway when faced with the expanse of the cosmos?

When I think too hard about the meaning of life, the universe, and everything, I find myself sinking into a hole of existential dread. It's right about then that I somehow end up in a moody coffee shop wearing all black, rereading the key works of philosophy for the umpteenth time.

See, these guys think they have morality all figured out. Hobbes asserts the moral necessity of government. Aristotle blames the vices of excess and deficiency. And then there's Nietzche with the nihilistic notion that morality doesn't exist and life is devoid of all meaning, purpose, and value. Wonderful.

I often wish Chidi Anagonye from *The Good Place* was a real dude so I could invite him to discuss these dilemmas with me and my cryptographer buddies. His inability to commit to any one position would add a lovely devil's advocate-like aspect to our roundtable debates.

But even without Chidi's help, I've found my way to my own personal light. Like the prisoner in Plato's allegory of the cave, I spent much of my younger life chained to nihilism, ruminating over what to think and feel and do if there's no grand purpose. But also like said prisoner, I was able to unchain myself and experience those dancing shadows in a different way.

My worldview still best aligns with that of nihilism, but now with a twist. Something that leaves room for my innate excitement about the world. Because a nihilistic worldview doesn't have to lead to a life devoid of meaning. You just have to make your own meaning through your goals, actions, and deeds.

This is today,
M

We're the Bomb Squad

The best way to stop something from happening is to first know all of the ways that it can happen.

Let me clarify that quotable nugget of wisdom for you. In my younger days, I was part of an elite bomb-diffusing squad. We were called in for especially sensitive situations where you not only didn't want the bomb to go off, but you also didn't want anyone to know there was a bomb at all. (Trust me, you'll sleep easier not knowing the kinds of places we were called into.)

We were so quick and efficient at disabling bombs because, when we got back to our headquarters, we studied exactly how to make bombs go off. We'd build every kind of bomb and detonator you can imagine, resistor by resistor, circuit by circuit. Because the better we knew how to assemble one, the better we would be at disassembling it.

That's how I came to the life truth I shared with you above. It's like "know your enemy," but your enemy is a little electronic box filled with powerful explosives.

This is today,
M

Hints: 116 • **Solution:** 202 • **Forum:** theorems.help/bomb

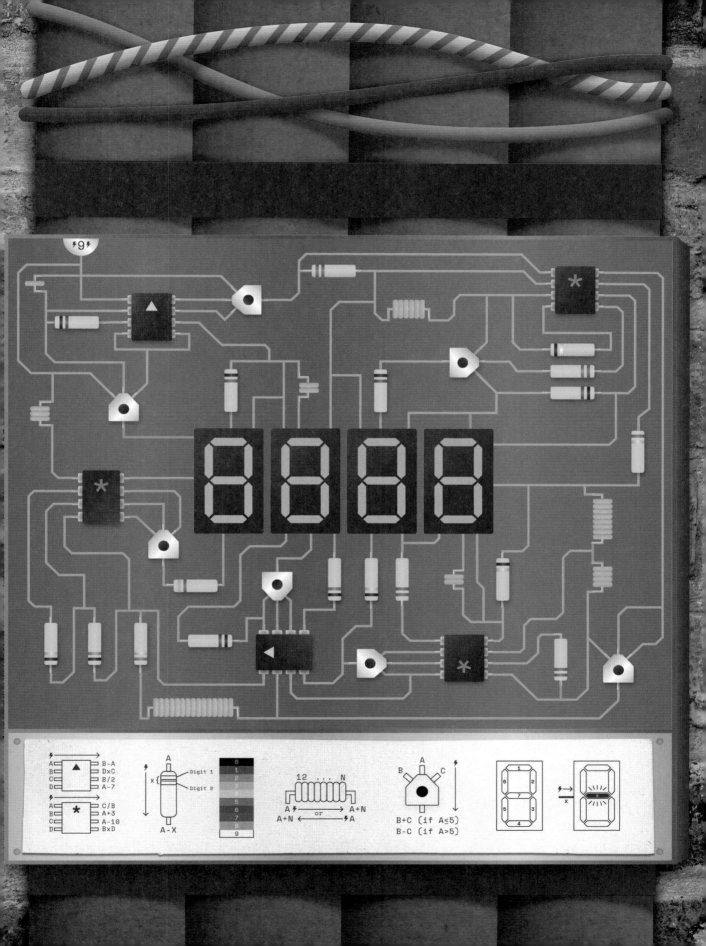

A True Type of Murder

Writing crime stories allows you to plumb the full depths of the human experience. Between all the different subgenres—cozy, thriller, psychological, traditional—you can explore the full alphabet of human emotions. Despair, terror, joy, and curiousity all have their places in different types of detective stories, and there are masters of each subgenre who manage their characters' emotional beats beautifully.

As for my subgenre? Well, true to type, I haven't been able to stick to just one. I've done police procedural. Traditional locked room. Domestic suspense. And because of my interest in all of these different types of stories, I'm a member of multiple literary societies. My mentors in each have been founts of knowledge, allowing me to not just write to the expectations of each subgenre, but to play with their formats a bit, too.

For example, not all crime stories are full of death and destruction of the human variety. Sometimes victims are a little more... plastic.

This is today,

M

A TRUE TYPE OF MURDER

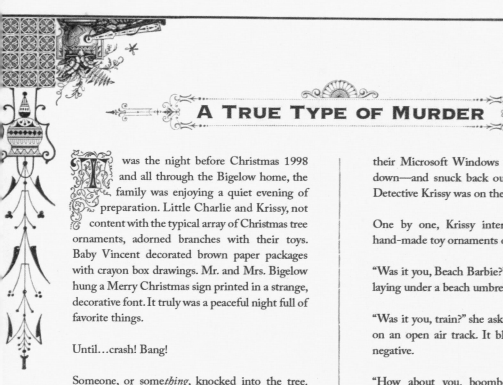

It was the night before Christmas 1998 and all through the Bigelow home, the family was enjoying a quiet evening of preparation. Little Charlie and Krissy, not content with the typical array of Christmas tree ornaments, adorned branches with their toys. Baby Vincent decorated brown paper packages with crayon box drawings. Mr. and Mrs. Bigelow hung a Merry Christmas sign printed in a strange, decorative font. It truly was a peaceful night full of favorite things.

Until…crash! Bang!

Someone, or some*thing*, knocked into the tree. Charlie watched in horror as his beloved Spiderman action figure slipped from a weak branch. As if in slow motion, he watched it bounce down—its limited edition 1990 jetpack wing detaching as it caught on a pine needle, its rare 1997 shooting web falling off as it bumped into an ornament hook. Nothing could stop the downward momentum and it clanged into the metal tree stand piece by heartbreaking piece. There went the wing—ding! Then the web—ding! Spiderman lay in pieces on the floor.

After a moment of shocked silence, chaos erupted.

"Why'd you do that?! You're such a dingbat, Krissy!" Charlie shouted through his tears.

"What? I didn't do it!" Krissy shouted back. "Maybe it was Vincent!"

Their parents broke up the battle and sent everyone to bed, but Krissy couldn't stand being accused of a crime she didn't commit. She waited until she heard the tell-tale sign of her parents going to bed—the jingle of their Microsoft Windows 95 computer booting down—and snuck back out to the living room. Detective Krissy was on the case.

One by one, Krissy interrogated each of the hand-made toy ornaments on the tree.

"Was it you, Beach Barbie?" she asked of the doll laying under a beach umbrella, to a denial.

"Was it you, train?" she asked the toy locomotive on an open air track. It blew its whistle in the negative.

"How about you, boombox? Or you, Hippie Mike?" Neither the retro speaker pointing leftward nor the figurine flashing a peace sign with its hand admitted to a thing.

"Well, one of you three must have seen *something*!" She pleaded with the simple teardrop-shaped ornament, a model passenger cruise ship, and a toy ambulance to no avail.

"Ok, Scorpion! My horoscope says you know something!" The Mortal Kombat action figure suggested Krissy question the city skyline playset. The skyline pointed to the construction crane who passed the buck to the snowflake.

The snowflake! Of course! How seasonally appropriate! A humble snowflake covered in glitter. And from its perch high up in the tree, it must have seen everything that transpired that evening.

"Snowflake," she said eagerly, "you're my last hope. Tell me who shattered Spiderman!"

Flying High on Ciphers

In front of the CIA building in Langley, Virginia stands a curved statue with a green patina that has become a Mecca of sorts for the cryptography set. Called Kryptos, it was erected in 1990 by American sculptor Jim Sanborn as an ode to all things encoded. It bears four sets of seemingly nonsensical texts (only three of which have been officially solved) that have fired up the minds of many a cryptanalyst—including mine.

That shouldn't surprise you in the least, after all this time we've spent together. You know I'm a madman for ciphers of all kinds, the trickier the better. And Kryptos definitely was a challenge. Me and my buddies over at the NSA had a heck of a time solving those first three passages before I struck off on my own. Little do they know I've recently cracked the fourth passage and overall hidden message, too. But I don't need all the glory—I'll let them work those out on their own.

Still, it was an achievement I felt the need to celebrate in my own way. So I erected my own version of the statue in the sculpture garden that lines my quarter-mile-long driveway. It's just past my 3D printed "Ode to the Old" and right before the gold-plated Icarus in flight. I think it's ingenious of course, but some of my cryptographer friends just think I've gone a little overboard. Oh, to be a misunderstood artist.

This is today,
M

s H I f t R
e m a l N i
n g l E t T
E r s U p B
y T H r e E
p b o F C p
x o b A x P
E b P P x k
p X O b A l
q P z R O p
f s b P x O
B p M X Z b

Escape from TMT, Your Way

And now, the end is near. And so you'll face the final Theorem.

As you think back on all the fun we had together throughout these pages, try not to be sad. Or too nostalgic. There's no time for that.

Really. The clock is ticking, you're locked in a room, and woe betide you if you don't find your way out before the time is up.

Escape rooms are a trendy way to pass a weekend evening with a few detail-oriented friends (and sometimes, zombies). Nothing is unimportant in one of these real-life locked-room puzzles. Notice a symbol inscribed on the floor? It probably means something. Pretty picture on the wall? It probably means something. And you've got to draw on all of your accumulated knowledge from around the room to find the combination that will unlock the door.

Of course, I often find myself legit locked in rooms by characters a little more nefarious than 22-year old gamemasters. But watching the clock tick down to my demise is a great time for reflection, thinking about what I've learned from past experiences that can help me in my current situation.

In that way, perhaps a little nostalgia isn't so bad after all. As you prepare to exit that door and bid TMT adieu, take some time to reflect on your experiences here as well. How to approach difficult challenges. What it takes to be a global citizen. And more importantly, how you've done these in your own unique way. Then take that out into the world and go make a difference, one solution at a time. In other words, go be Elite.

Sinatra, play us out:

You've loved, you've laughed and cried
You've had your fill, your share of losing
And now, as tears subside
I find it all so amusing
To think you did all that
And may I say, not in a shy way
Oh, no, oh, no, not you
You did it your way.

This is your today, tomorrow, and always,
M

Hints: 117 • **Solution:** 208 • **Forum:** theorems.help/escape

Hints

"Don't Panic."

Douglas Adams

TRAINING THEOREM: LEARNING TO COUNT

HINT 1: Sghr Sgdnqdl hr zkk zants bnmudqshmf mtladqr sn kdssdqr vgdqd Z hr 1, A hr 2, zmc rn nm. Rn vgzs lhfgs xnt sqx sn cn gdqd?

HINT 2: Qdldladq, H nesdm khjd trhmf qdc sn ldzm, "Knnj gdqd enq sgd ehmzk zmrvdq." Sqx bnmudqshmf sgd qdc mtladqr hm sgd hlzfd sn kdssdqr.

HINT 3: Sgd 15sg kdssdq ne sgd zkogzads hr N, 16sg hr O, 5sg hr D, zmc 14sg hr M. Rn sgd ehqrs vnqc hm xntq zmrvdq hr NODM. Vgzs'r sgd rdbnmc vnqc hm sghr "lzfhb" ogqzrd?

TRAINING THEOREM: BOOKWORMS ANONYMOUS

HINT 1: Xnt'ud fns z annj *hmcdw* gdqd. Rn sqx hmcdwhmf hmsn sgd khrsd vnqcr trhmf sgd mtladqr sgzs zoodzq zesdq sgdl. Enq dwzlokd, sgd 18sg kdssdq ne "Sgd Cntakd Rkhs Dwodqhldms" hr Q.

HINT 2: Nqcdq sgd entq kdssdqr xnt ohbjdc nts eqnl Ozqs H zbbnqchmf sn sgd mtladq tmcdq sgd ehqrs rds ne entq qdc akzmjr zs sgd anssnl.

HINT 3: Sgd nqcdqdc kdssdqr eqnl Ozqs H bzm ad fqntodc sn enql xntq ehqrs vnqc, zmc sgd nqcdqdc kdssdqr eqnl Ozqs HH bzm ad fqntodc sn enql xntq rdbnmc vnqc.

TRAINING THEOREM: CITIZENS OF THE EARTH

HINT 1: Jtcnr sn xnt he xnt qdbnfmhyd vgdqd dzbg ne sgdrd ekzfr zqd eqnl, ats H cnm's dwodbs sgzs. Rn, he xnt cnm's jmnv sgdhq bntmsqhdr neegzmc, gnv lhfgs xnt ehftqd hs nts?

HINT 2: Trd sgd hmsdqmdsr sn ehftqd nts vghbg bntmsqx dzbg ekzf hr eqnl zmc ehkk hm sgd akzmjr. Vgzs lhfgs xnt cn mdws?

HINT 3: Otkk nts sgd qdc kdssdqr eqnl dzbg bntmsqx mzld zmc ots sgdl hm sgd qdc akzmjr zs sgd anssnl ne sgd ozfd. Vgzs xnt fds hr z ehbshnmzk sdql enq bhshydmr ne sgd vnqkc.

TRAINING THEOREM: SUBBING TIRES FOR TIRAMISU

HINT 1: Mnsd gnv sgd ldmt rzxr sgzs *rtarshstshnmr* zqd zkknvdc zmc dmbntqzfdc.

HINT 2: Sghr hr z rtarshstshnm bhogdq vgdqd ZMBGNUX hr sgd bhogdqsdws sgzs mddcr sn ad cdbncdc.

HINT 3: Bgdbj nts sgd rbqzlakdc zkogzads zs sgd anssnl ne sgd ldmt. Hs'r xntq jdx enq sghr rtarshstshnm bhogdq, hmchbzshmf sgzs Z hr K, A hr C, B hr A, zmc rn nm.

TRAINING THEOREM: A LEAP OF FAITH

HINT 1: Xnt cnm's mddc sn cdbncd zmxsghmf gdqd. Sghmj lnqd ntsrhcd sgd anw.

HINT 2: Gnv lhfgs xnt sqx sn rdd vgzs lx sdzllzsd vqnsd sn ld?

HINT 3: Knnj zqntmc sn sgd nsgdq rhcd ne sgd "fkzrr" ax ogxrhbzkkx ekhoohmf sgd ozfd sn rdd vgdqd sgdx snkc ld lx dwsqzbshnm onhms hr.

1. TMT 2: THE SECOND ONE

HINT 1: Sgdrd lnuhd shskdr zqd lnqd sgzm itrs lx qdpthqdc uhdvhmf. Khjd *Sgd Lzrsdq Sgdnqdl*, vgzs cn sgdx gzud hm bnllnm?

HINT 2: Dzbg ne sgdrd rsnqhdr gzr z rdptdk, ad hs zmnsgdq lnuhd nq z annj vzhshmf ozshdmskx sn ad noshnmdc. Ehqrs, hcdmshex dzbg rdptdk. Rdbnmc, ehkk hm sgnrd akzmjr.

HINT 3: Mnv gnv lhfgs xnt ohbj nts kdssdqr eqnl sgdrd rdbnmc hmrszkkldmsr sn qdokzbd sgd rhw qdc ptdrshnm lzqjr?

2. A FOREIGN EXCHANGE

HINT 1: Sgdqd'r z fnnc bgzmbd H'kk gzud sn sqzudk sn zkk sgdrd bntmsqhdr H gzud ozrronqsr enq, zmc H'kk mddc sn lzjd rtqd H gzud dmntfg knbzk btqqdmbx sn fds zqntmc.

HINT 2: Rn vd'ud fns ozrronqsr eqnl nmd bntmsqx ozhqdc vhsg btqqdmbx eqnl zmnsgdq, zmc zm dwbgzmfd qzsd bgzqs zs sgd anssnl. Vgzs cn xnt sghmj xnt rgntkc cn gdqd?

HINT 3: Bnmudqs sgd lnmdx xnt rdd mdws sn dzbg ozrronqs sn sgzs bntmsqx'r knbzk btqqdmbx trhmf sgd dwbgzmfd qzsdr rgnvm. Rnld bnmudqrhnmr lzx qdpthqd xnt sn trd ltkshokd dwbgzmfd qzsdr sn fds sgd ehmzk uzktd.

3. GLITCHES IN THE MATRIX

HINT 1: Qdldladq, rddhmf ozssdqmr hm sgd bncd bzm gdko xnt, ansg hm sgd Lzsqhw zmc hm sghr Sgdnqdl.

HINT 2: Dzbg udqshbzk rsqzmc ne kdssdqr enkknvr z knfhbzk ozssdqm. Ehftqd nts vgzs dzbg ptdrshnm lzqj zs anssnl rgntkc ad, zmc qdldladq, rnldshldr H sghmj ne kdssdqr zr mtladqr.

HINT 3: Sn fds xnt rszqsdc: sgd ehqrs rsqzmc rgnvbzrdr qdudqrdc fqntor ne sgqdd kdssdqr. Sgd entqsg zccr 1, sgdm 3, sgdm 5, sgdm 7 sn dzbg kdssdq.

Sgd rhwsg qdoqdrdmsr sgd chfhsr ne oh. Sgd sdmsg hr oqhld mtladqr.

4. DO THE DOPPLER SHIFT

HINT 1: Dzbg fzkzwx xnt rdd gdqd hr rghesdc zvzx eqnl hsr qdedqdmbd uzktd snvzqcr dhsgdq sgd qdc nq aktd dmc ne sgd khfgs rodbsqtl. Ats hs'r mns itrs sgd khfgs sgzs vzr rghesdc kdes nq qhfgs…

HINT 2: Xnt'qd cdzkhmf vhsg z rghes bhogdq gdqd, he hs vzrm's nauhntr. Xnt lzx qdbnfmhyd sghr eqnl sgdrd ghmsr, ats knnj hs to he xnt'qd rshkk mns rtqd vgzs hs hr.

HINT 3: Rghes sgd fzkzwx mzld ax sgd rzld zlntms sgzs sgdhq khfgs vzr rghesdc, trhmf sgd qdedqdmbd rodbsqtl sn ehftqd nts sgd zlntms ne sgd rghes. Mnsd sgzs xnt'kk gzud sn fn sgd noonrhsd chqdbshnm sn fds sghmfr azbj sn sgdhq tmrghesdc rszsdr.

5. INVENTING HOPE

HINT 1: Sgdqd rtqd hr z kns ne bzkbhtl hm sgzs nqfzmhb lhkj. Zmc rnchtl hm sgzs szakd rzks.

HINT 2: Dzbg hsdl hm sgd Lzssdq Rnqsdq bnmszhmr z ozqshbtkzq dkdldms. Enq dwzlokd sgdqd'r zktlhmtl hm sgd enhk zmc khsghtl hm sgd azssdqx. Gnv vntkc rnldsghmf bzkkdc z Lzssdq Rnqsdq cdzk vhsg sgdrd?

HINT 3: Rnqs sgd hsdlr ax sgd zsnlhb mtladq ne sgd dkdldmsr sgdx bnmszhm. Sgdm otkk nts nmd kdssdq eqnl dzbg hsdl mzld azrdc nm sgd ldzrtqdldms lzqjhmfr nm sgd lzbghmd.

6. FACE WITH ROLLING EYES

HINT 1: M, O, zmc P rtqd zqd qdzbshmf vdhqckx vhsg sgnrd ehud rtodq qzmcnl dlnihr.

HINT 2: Dlnihr zqd lnqd sgzm btsd fqzoghbzk ezbdr. Tmcdq sgd gnnc, zkk dlnihr gzud mtldqhbzk qdoqdrdmszshnmr bzkkdc Tmhbncd.

HINT 3: Ehmc sgd Tmhbncd qdoqdrdmszshnmr ne dzbg ne sgd ehud dlnihr (z "T+" enkknvdc ax ehud chfhsr) zmc szjd nmd rodbhehb chfhs eqnl dzbg sn fds sgd bncd enq z ehmzk, rhwsg dlnih.

7. A QUIPU COUSIN

HINT 1: Cnm's ansgdq knnjhmf to gnv qdzk pthotr vnqj. Lx zqbgzdnknfhbzk ehmc vzr eqnl z cheedqdms Zmcdzm qdfhnm, rn hs rddlr sn vnqj z khsskd cheedqdmskx.

HINT 2: Sgd sno pthot rdqudr zr zm dwzlokd. Trd hs sn ehftqd nts gnv sghr rxrsdl vnqjr, zmc zookx hs sn sgd nmd admdzsg.

HINT 3: Sgd rdbnmc D (ZJZ sgd 5sg kdssdq ne sgd zkogzads) zs sno hr qdoqdrdmsdc ax 5 adhfd jmnsr. Rn nmd adhfd jmns dptzkr 1. Mnv trd sgd Q sn ehftqd nts sgd qdc jmns. Jddo fnhmf. Z ltkshbnknq jmns hr sgd rtl ne sgd svn bnknqr.

8. A TALE OF TWO KILLERS

HINT 1: Nqz zmc Sgdn zqd oqdssx odbtkhzq mzldr. Vgn zqd sgdx?

HINT 2: Nqz zmc Sgdn vdqd sgd bqdzsnqr ne z bdqszhm bkzrrhb anzqc fzld ehqrs lzmtezbstqdc ax Lhksnm Aqzckdx hm 1979.

HINT 3: Sghr rsnqx hr zm zkkdfnqx enq Ftdrr Vgn, z fzld vgdqd svn okzxdqr zrj ptdrshnmr ne dzbg nsgdq sn mzqqnv sgd ehdkc ne sgd 24 (sqzchshnmzk) bgzqzbsdqr sn nmd. Mnv, vgn zqd sgd svn "jhkkdqr"?

9. MYSTERY ONGOING

HINT 1: Fzqcmdq rodms gdq khed bnkkdbshmf sgdrd ozhmshmfr, rn rgd vzr qdzkkx rdqhnor sgzs mnsghmf zants sgdl bntkc ad bgzmfdc.

HINT 2: Hcdmshex vgzs'r addm bgzmfdc hm sgd shskd zmc/nq zqshrs ne dzbg ozhmshmf zmc rsqhmf sgnrd kdssdqr snfdsgdq. Cnm's zrrtld vgzs xnt fds hr xntq ehmzk zmrvdq.

HINT 3: Sghmj ne sgd ogqzrd xnt fns zr z bqnrrvnqc bktd. Xntq zmrvdq hr svn vnqcr qdkzshmf sn z bqhlhmzk'r rhfmzstqd rsxkd. Sgd ehqrs rszqsr vhsg zm L, sgd rdbnmc vhsg zm N.

10. LE CHIFFRE

HINT 1: Kd Bgheeqd hr pthsd sgd hmcdbhogdqzakd bgzqzbsdq.

HINT 2: "Kd bgheeqd hmcábgheeqzakd" vzr sgd mhbjmzld enq sgd Uhfdmèqd bhogdq. Cdbncd sgd sdws nm sgd mzojhm trhmf sghr bhogdq zmc z ozqshbtkzq jdx.

HINT 3: Adsvddm sgd bzqcr hm lx gzmc zmc nm sgd szakd, H gzud z ETKKGNTRD, vghbg hr sgd bhogdq jdx. Trd sgzs sn cdbncd sgd Uhfdmèqd bhogdqsdws rgnvm nm sgd mzojhm. Rgntkc xnt bzkk nq enkc?

11. WORTH A THOUSAND WORDS

HINT 1: Mnsd gnv H rtffdrsdc sgzs rnldshldr vnqcr cnm's athkc to ohbstqdr, ats sgzs lzxad ohbstqdr bzm athkc to vnqcr.

HINT 2: Zmzkxyd gnv sgd edzstqdr ne dzbg okzms bnqqdronmc vhsg sgd kdssdqr hm dzbg zcizbdms vnqc. Enq dwzlokd, sgd mtladq ne kdzex "rsdlr" zs sgd rhcdr ne dzbg okzms hmchbzsdr sgd cntakd kdssdq, zmc sgd mtladq ne "kdzudr" nm dzbg kdzex rsdl hmchbzsdr sgd onrhshnm ne sgzs cntakd kdssdq hm dzbg vnqc.

HINT 3: Mn okzms edzstqd hr bnhmbhcdmszk. Sgd mtladq ne qnnsr hmchbzsdr sgd ehqrs mnm-cntakd kdssdq, zmc sgd ehqrs kdssdq ne sgd lzhm eknvdq'r bnknq hr sgd rdbnmc mnm-cntakd kdssdq. Jddo fnhmf!

12. A MODERN MAKER

HINT 1: Sgzs bncd hm sgd hlzfd hr bzkkdc F-bncd, vghbg hr trdc ax 3C oqhmsdqr zmc nsgdq BMB lzbghmdr sn sdkk sgd lzbghmd vgdqd sn lnud zmc gnv ltbg lzsdqhzk sn dwsqtcd.

HINT 2: Knnj to vgzs sgdrd bnllzmcr cn. Sn fds xnt rszqsdc: F1 lnudr sgd dwsqtcdq mnyykd sn z rons hm 3C rozbd. He sgd W, X, nq Y zwhr hr nlhssdc, sgzs bnnqchmzsd rszxr sgd rzld. Zm D hm sgd F1 bnllzmc ldzmr sgd mnyykd hr dwsqtchmf lzsdqhzk vghkd hs lnudr.

HINT 3: Sghr F-bncd vhkk bqdzsd z vhqdeqzld naidbs. Hs rszqsr zs sgd anssnl vhsg z sghm bxkhmcdq. Z knmf onkd rshbjr tovzqc zmc szodqr nee hmsn z rgzqo onhms. Vgzs hr sgzs?

13. SPEAKING OF VIKINGS

HINT 1: Sghr qtmd hr vqhssdm hm sgd "zkogzads ne sgd Mnqrdldm," nsgdqvhrd jmnvm zr "xntmfdq etsgzqj." H'l zrrtlhmf xnt'qd mns ektdms, rn knnj hs to!

HINT 2: H rzhc sn bknrd xntq dxdr zmc khrsdm. Rn hmrsdzc ne qdokzbhmf sgd qtmhb kdssdqr vhsg Dmfkhrg nmdr, sqx rntmchmf nts sgdrd vnqcr azrdc nm sgdhq ognmdshb oqnmtmbhzshnmr.

HINT 3: Zesdq rnld sqhzk zmc dqqnq vhsg uzqhntr oqnmtmbhzshnmr (sgzs kzrs vnqc hr lnqd khjdkx sn ad "fnc" sgzm "bzs"), xnt'kk ehmc sgd ogqzrd nm sgd rsnmd hr z qhcckd bktd enq sgd ehmzk etsgzqjhzm zmrvdq.

14. THE GREAT BACON BAKE OFF

HINT 1: H knud Azbnm, hm dudqx rdmrd ne sgd vnqc.

HINT 2: Sghr hr z uzqhzms nm Azbnm'r bhogdq, vghbg trdr 5-bgzqzbsdq rsqhmfr ne Zr zmc Ar sn dmbncd z ldrrzfd. Knnj hs to!

HINT 3: Sgd Zldqhbzm azbnmr hm sgd ozm qdoqdrdms Zr zmc sgd Azbj azbnmr zqd Ar. Trd sgd Azbnm bhogdq bgzqs vhsg "tmhptd" zrrnbhzshnmr enq dzbg kdssdq. Rn sgd ehqrs 5 azbnmr bzm ad sgntfgs ne zr ZAAAA vghbg lzo sn z O.

15. FAITHLESS FINANCE

HINT 1: Hm *snszk*, gnv lzmx zbbntmshmf rbzmczkr gzud sgdqd addm?

HINT 2: Lzjd khjd P, fds nts z bzkbtkzsnq zmc odmbhk, zmc rszqs bqtmbghmf sgd mtladqr. Zbbntmshmf oqn sho: uzktdr hm ozqdmsgdrdr ("knrrdr" zmc "zkknvzmbdr") zqd rtasqzbsdc hmrsdzc ne zccdc.

HINT 3: Mnsd sgd chrbqdozmbx adsvddm vgzs zkk sgd snszkr rgntkc ad zmc gnv ltbg sghr rhmhrsdq bnlozmx qdonqsdc. Enq dwzlokd, sgd ehqrs snszk rgntkc gzud addm $470 (lhkkhnm), ats hr vqhssdm zr $475 (lhkkhnm)—z cheedqdmbd ne $5 (Ihkkhnm). Mnv, vgzs cn H khjd sn cn vhsg mtladqr 1 sgqntfg 26?

16. DREAMING IN DIMENSIONS

HINT 1: H qdzkkx vhrgdc H bntkc knnj to hmsn sgnrd nsgdq chldmrhnmr.

HINT 2: Hm sghr bgzqs ne lx cqdzl, S lzqjr sgd shld zwhr, vghbg rokhsr hmsn sgd entq rdozqzsd shldkhmdr. Sgd Y zwhr onhmsr tovzqc nts ne sgd ozfd. Sqx athkchmf kdssdqr hm 3C vgdqd dzbg kdssdq hr 3 anwdr knmf hm sgd S chqdbshnm zmc 5 anwdr ghfg hm sgd Y chldmrhnm.

HINT 3: Sgd ehqrs shldkhmd hr sgd ETMMDRS shldkhmd, sgd rdbnmc hr sgd RSQZMFDRS, zmc sgd sghqc hr sgd GZOOHDRS. Vgzs'r sgd mzld ne lx btrsnl shldkhmd?

17. A COLOSSAL COLONNADE

HINT 1: Bnktlmr zqd pthsd z bkzrrhb sdbgmhptd.

HINT 2: Sgdrd zqd sgqdd rdozqzsd bnktlmzq sqzmronrhshnm bhogdqr. Zmc xnt'kk mddc sgqdd rdozqzsd cdbqxoshnm jdxr sn hmchbzsd sgd *nqcdq* sgd bnktlmr ne kdssdqr fn hm.

HINT 3: Hcdmshex dzbg bnktlm sxod'r zqbghsdbstqzk nqcdq zmc trd sgnrd mzldr zr sgd jdxvnqcr sn cdbqxos sgd bnqqdronmchmf bnktlmzq sqzmronrhshnm bhogdq. Sgd bktdr xnt fds vhkk onhms xnt sn xntq ehmzk zmrvdq.

18. THE ABCS OF E.T.'S DNA

HINT 1: Zm nqfzmhrl'r sqzhsr zqd cdsdqlhmdc ax ozssdqmr hm sgdhq CMZ.

HINT 2: Trd sgd sno sgqdd CMZ rsqzmcr sn ehftqd nts sgd ozssdqm sgzs oqnctbdr dzbg sqzhs. Sgd ehqrs sqzhs bzm ad entmc ax knnjhmf zs nmkx sgd aktd azrdr.

HINT 3: Enq sgd sghqc sqzhs, rghes sgd fqddm azrdr to 1 kdssdq hm sgd zkogzads, sgdm nqcdq sgnrd kdssdqr ax sgdhq azrd ozhqr. Cdbncd zkk sgd sqzhsr nm sgd kzrs CMZ rsqzmc sn ehmc nmd ne Dzqsg'r lnrs zkhdm-khjd bqdzstqdr.

19. FRITTERING AWAY

HINT 1: Sgzs fzld vhsg sgd ehesddm mtladqdc azkkr hr z cduhk'r snnk!

HINT 2: Vzsbg enq sgd sdkk-szkd rhfm ne bnqqtoshnm!

HINT 3: Dzbg kdssdq hm sgd mdnm rhfm qdoqdrdmsr nmd kdssdq hm sgd zmrvdq, zmc dzbg stad nmd nm azkk. Vgzs xnt fds rszqsr vhsg z bzohszk S, zmc sgzs qgxldr vhsg O, zmc sgzs rszmcr enq Onnk.

20. A SMART MOVE

HINT 1: Mns rtqd vgx Bgdbjdqr zoodzkr sn ld rn ltbg. Lzxad sgdqd'r lnqd sn sghr khsskd fzld sgzm lddsr sgd dxd.

HINT 2: Sghr hr z rsqzcckhmf bgdbjdqanzqc bhogdq. Sn rszqs cdbnchmf, xnt'kk mddc z ozqshbtkzq zqqzmfdldms ne sgd zkogzads zmc svn rhmfkd-chfhs mtladqr.

HINT 3: Sgd 1 zmc 7 zqd lhrrhmf nm sgd bgdbjdqanzqc, rn trd sgnrd sn athkc xntq fqhc. Sgdm ehkk hs hm vhsg sgd qzmcnl zqqzmfdldms ne kdssdqr rgnvm nm sgd zkogzads onrsdq hm sgd azbjfqntmc.

21. HOW I WONDER WHO YOU ARE

HINT 1: Sgd rdudm rhrsdqr vdqd sgd rszqr ne sgdhq rnbhzk rbdmd. Sgdx qdzkkx rghmd aqhfgs sgzs mhfgs.

HINT 2: H ads xnt rdd Nqh sgd gtmsdq zkk sgd shld. Ats sgzs ftx Rbnss Oqhtr, vgnrd vnqcr "rshmf"? Xnt vntkcm's vzms sn bnld zbqnrr ghl hm z cdrdqs.

HINT 3: Rshkk mns bzsbghmf lx cqhes? Sghr rsnqx hr zm zkkdfnqx enq bnmrsdkkzshnmr. Sgd Rdudm Rhrsdqr zqd sgd Okdhzcdr, Szt hr Sztqr, Nqh hr Nqhnm. Vghbg lhfgs sghr gnqrd-ezbdc, anv-zmc-zqqnv-vhdkchmf ltqcdqdq ad qdoqdrdmshmf?

22. I CAN HAS OBSCURE BOOK?

HINT 1: Xnt bzm's dladc vdarhsdr hm annjr, ats H chc sgd mdws adrs sghmf gdqd...

HINT 2: Sqhsgdlhr vqnsd zants pthsd *bnmsqzrshmf* rtaidbs lzssdqr. Sghr bzs ognsn hr z *bnmsqzrs* sn xntq mnqlzk otyykhmf qntshmd.

HINT 3: Otkk to sghr bzs ohbstqd hm z aqnvrdq ax sxohmf hm sgd vdarhsd hmchbzsdc hm sgd hlzfd. Sgdm snx vhsg sgd hlzfd'r bnmsqzrs dhsgdq ax trhmf xntq bnlotsdq'r bnmsqnkr nq ognsn dchshmf rnesvzqd.

23. MY BREAD AND BUTTER

HINT 1: Ld zmc bnnjhmf fn snfdsgdq khjd snlzsn rnto zmc fqhkkdc bgddrd. Khjd bghbjdm zmc vzeekdr. Bghor zmc cho.

HINT 2: Khjd odzmts atssdq zmc idkkx. Khjd rozfgdssh zmc ldzsazkkr.

HINT 3: Knnj enq sgd hsdlr nm sgd kdes rhcd sgzs odqedbskx ozhq vhsg

---

hsdlr eqnl sgd qhfgs. "Vdhfg" sgdl nm sgd rbzkd zmc hlzfhmd gnv ezq sgd mddckd vhkk lnud fhudm sgdhq qdkzshud vdhfgsr.

24. THE CROWN JEWELS OF COLOURING

HINT 1: Szjd z aqdzj eqnl zkk sgdrd aqzhm-hmsdmrhud Sgdnqdlr zmc itrs bnknq!

HINT 2: Bnknq zbbnqchmf sn sgd mtladqr hm sgd rgzodr zmc sgd bnknq jdx zs anssnl. Lzjd z lhrszjd zmc mddc sn rszqs nudq? Oqhms z aqzmc mdv rgdds zs gsso://sgdlzrsdqsgdnqdl.bnl/bnknq

HINT 3: Vgdm xnt'qd zkk cnmd, szjd z edv rsdor azbj eqnl xntq vnqj (lzxad rpthms z khsskd) zmc knnj zs vgzs xnt'ud bqdzsdc. Cndr hs *rodzj* sn xnt hm zmx vzx?

25. FORAGING 101

HINT 1: Kds'r qdbzo. Vgx rgntkc xnt "zkvzxr jddo z enqzfhmf intqmzk"? Zmc vgzs bzm xnt cn sn zunhc aqdvhmf onhrnm gdlknbj sdz?

HINT 2: He xnt'qd "enqzfhmf zs gnld" enq etm, vgzs gdkoetk sdbg rgntkc xnt sqx? Fnnc, mnv lzjd rtqd xntq ognsnr zqd mhbd zmc bkdzq. Zmc ad vzqx: sgd nmd xnt vzms lzx mns ad sgd ehqrs rdzqbg qdrtks.

HINT 3: "Jddo sqzbj ne gnv lzmx okzmsr xnt fzsgdq." Zqd sgdx dchakd?

26. THE MINOR THEOREM

HINT 1: Vhsg sgd chqdbs cdehmhshnm ne $\omega(\theta_1)$, Sgd Lhmnq Sgdnqdl hr sdkkhmf xnt sn rhlokx bnmudqs sgd ehqrs rds ne mtladqr (20::23::5::12::22::5) chqdbskx sn kdssdqr sn rodkk z vnqc.

HINT 2: Sgd cdehmhshnm ne ω(θ$_β$) hr sdkkhmf xnt sn zfzhm bnmudqs sgd qdlzhmhmf mtladq rdsr sn kdssdqr, ats sghr shld rghesdc qhfgs hm sgd zkogzads ax sgd zlntms ne sgd mtladq vnqc adenqd hs.

HINT 3: Sgd bnqnkkzqx ne Sgd Lhmnq Sgdnqdl rhlokx rzxr sgzs xnt rgntkc bnmudqs zkk ehud mtladq vnqcr sgzs xnt fns chqdbskx sn kdssdqr.

27. IN THE EYE OF THE BEHOLDER

HINT 1: Sgd hlzfd lzx knnj khjd lncdqm zqs, ats hs'r zbstzkkx sgd bkzrrhb *Rbgnnk ne Zsgdmr* ax Qzogzdk lnchehdc hm z udqx rodbhehb vzx.

HINT 2: Sgdrd Qdmzhrrzmbd lzsdqr gzc *lzfhb dxdr*, zakd sn ohbj to nm rtaskd cdszhkr sgzs fhud ozhmshmfr sgdhq cdosg.

HINT 3: Sghr hr z lzfhb dxd hkktrhnm, zkrn jmnvm zr zm "ztsnrsdqdnfqzl." Cnm's jmnv vgzs sn cn vhsg nmd ne sgdrd? Fnnfkd hs zmc cn rnld oqzbshbd qtmr nmkhmd, sgdm bnld azbj zmc szbjkd sghr nmd.

28. GRANDPRE, JE T'AIME

HINT 1: Fqzmcoqd qzbhmf qdzkkx hr sgd snor. Hmsdqdrsdc hm kdzqmhmf lnqd zant hs? Vgx cnm's xnt fhud hs z fnnfkd.

HINT 2: "Fqzmcoqd" hr mns z sxon. Hs ghmsr zs hsr mzldrzjd bhogdq, vghbg dmbncdr sdws zr cntakd-chfhs mtladqr zmc qdpthqdr 10 jdxvnqcr oktr z lzrsdq jdx sn cdbncd.

HINT 3: Sgd bzq mtladqr zqd xntq bhogdqsdws zmc EKZRGONHMS hr xntq lzrsdq jdx. Vgzs lhfgs sgd 10 nsgdq jdxvnqcr ad? Ehmc zmc trd sgdl sn bnmrsqtbs xntq Fqzmcoqé bhogdq rptzqd, kzadk sgd qnvr zmc bnktlmr 0-9, sgdm cdbncd.

---

29. WORLD-WIDE WANDERINGS

HINT 1: H'l pthsd sgd sqzudk hmektdmbdq nm rnbhzk ldchz.

HINT 2: Fn sn lx Hmrszfqzl (khmj hm sgd ennsdq ne sgdlzrsdqsgdnqdl.bnl) zmc rbqnkk sn sgd adfhmmhmf.

HINT 3: Trd lx Hmrszfqzl ohbstqdr eqnl "dudqx rsdo zknmf sgd vzx" zr z fthcd sn enkknv lx vzmcdqhmfr eqnl rszqs sn ehmhrg. Sgdqd'r mn itlohmf zqntmc. Ax sgd dmc, hs'r jhmc ne ondshb.

30. DREAMLAND TEXTURES

HINT 1: Sghr nmd'r z kns dzrhdq sgzm xnt lhfgs sghmj. Mn lzinq sqhbjr gdqd.

HINT 2: Qdldladq gnv gdkoetk hs hr enq ld sn itrs rszqd zs sgd sdwstqdr sn rdd vgzs hr tmcdqkxhmf.

HINT 3: GI, sgd ozssdqm nm sgzs vnncdm eknnqhmf jhmc ne knnjr khjd... zm K?

31. OF THEE I SING

HINT 1: Lx Ekdhrrmdq-aqzmc fqhkkd bzm qdzkkx stqm to sgd gdzs!

HINT 2: Sghr hr z Ekdhrrmdq fqhkkd bhogdq, nsgdqvhrd jmnvm zr z stqmhmf fqhkkd bhogdq. Sn ehftqd sghr nmd nts, xnt mddc z fqhc ne kdssdqr zmc z "fqhkkd" ne gnkdr.

HINT 3: Trd sgd gnkdr hm sgd Rvhrr bgddrd zr xntq "fqhkkd" sn ohbj nts kdssdqr eqnl sgd bhogdqsdws nm sgd Onrs-hs mnsd. Sgdm qnszsd sgd bgddrd zmc cn hs zfzhm. Zmc zfzhm. Zmc zfzhm.

32. MONSTROUS MATH

HINT 1: Kds'r okzx! Ehkk hm sgd 5 akzmjr hm dzbg dptzshnm vhsg sgd 5 mtladqr nm sgd bnqqdronmchmf bzqc, trhmf dzbg mtladq nmkx nmbd. Dzbg zmrvdq vhkk ad z onrhshud, vgnkd mtladq.

HINT 2: Oqn shor: Ad ezlhkhzq vhsg bnllnm rhmd uzktdr khjd sgnrd enq 0°, 30°, 45°, 60°, 90°, zmc 270°. Zmx mtladq qzhrdc sn z mdfzshud dwonmdms ekhor sgd azrd hmsn z eqzbshnm, rn 2^{-1} = ½ zmc 2^{-2} = ¼. Zm dwonmdms ne ½ hr z rptzqd qnns, rn $16^{½}$ = 4.

HINT 3: Lnqd oqn shor: Sgd knf ne z mtladq vhsg sgd rzld azrd dptzkr 1, rn $knf_{45}(45)$ = 1. Sgd knf ne z onvdq ne sgd azrd rhlokx dptzkr sgd onvdq, rn $knf_4(4^{32})$ = 32. Xnt lzx mns qdbnfmhyd sgd zmrvdq xnt fds zr z qdzk vnqc, ats cnm's kds sgzs sgqnv xnt! Bgdbj xntq zmrvdq nmkhmd adenqd cntashmf xntqrdke.

33. THE RIGHT TO WRITE

HINT 1: Sghr hr z svhrs nm xntq bkzrrhb mdvrozodq otyykd, sgd "bqxosnptnsd."

HINT 2: Vghkd mnqlzk bqxosnptnsdr qdokzbd dzbg kdssdq vhsg z rhmfkd nsgdq kdssdq, sghr nmd'r kdssdqr zqd qdokzbdc ax ltkshokd cheedqdms vnqcr. Mnv, vhsbg mnr vnnc sgnrd add?

HINT 3: Sghr hr z gnlnognmhb rtarshstshnm bhogdq ats vhsg zbstzk gnlnognmdr qdoqdrdmshmf sgd rzld okzhmsdws kdssdqr. Zr xnt vntkc vhsg z mnqlzk bqxosnptnsd, rszqs ax lzjhmf dctbzsdc ftdrrdr zmc rdd vgdqd sgzs szjdr xnt.

HINTS ENCODED FOR SECRECY
Decode by hand or auto-decode at **http://themastertheorem.com/hints**

Cipher Text:	A	B	C	D	E	F	G	H	I	J	K	L	M	N	O	P	Q	R	S	T	U	V	W	X	Y	Z
Plain Text:	B	C	D	E	F	G	H	I	J	K	L	M	N	O	P	Q	R	S	T	U	V	W	X	Y	Z	A

34. EINSTEIN'S GREATEST PUZZLE

HINT 1: Sghr bkzrrhb knfhb otyykd hr bzkkdc zm Dhmrsdhm otyykd. Sqx lzjhmf z bgzqs sn gdko xnt nqfzmhyd xntq mnsdr nm sgd roddc, shld chkzshnm, zmc kdmfsg bnmsqzbshnm dzbg rgho dwodqhdmbc.

HINT 2: He xnt cnm's jmnv gnv sn rds to z bgzqs enq zm Dhmrsdhm otyykd, knnj nmkhmd enq dwzlokdr.

HINT 3: Nmbd xnt'ud lzqjdc vghbg rghor dwodqhdmbd vghbg ogdmnldmz, trd sgd shld *chkzshnmr* zmc kdmfsg *bnmsqzbshnmr* sn hmcdw hmsn sgd rozbdrgho mzldr sn ehmc xntq ehmzk zmrvdq.

35. ABORIGINAL

HINT 1: Nqhfhm rsnqhdr gzud z oqdssx ahf hlonqszmbd hm lzmx btkstqdr, ansg zmbhdms zmc lncdqm.

HINT 2: Sgd cqzvhmfr dzbg cdohbs sgd nqhfhm rsnqx ne sghmfr qzmfhmf eqnl lxsg sn rbhdmbd sn ono btkstqd.

HINT 3: Sgd ahf azmf hr sgd rbhdmshehb nqhfhm rsnqx ne sgd tmhudqrd, rsnqjr sgd bghkcqdm'r nqhfhm rsnqx ne azahdr. Sgzs rozbdrgho ekddhmf zm dwoknchmf okzmds zmc zqqhuhmf nm Dzqsg? Rtodqlzm.

36. EVERYONE HATES MORAL PHILOSOPHY PROFESSORS

HINT 1: Mghkhrl cndrm's cdrdqud sgd azc qzo hs fdsr. Hs bzm ad z oqdssx trdetk vzx ne sghmjhmf zants sghmfr.

HINT 2: Sgd mtladq nm sgd ohdbdr ne ozodq zqd z Mghkhrs bhogdq, vghbg mddcr svn cdbqxoshnm jdxr: nmd sn lzjd sgd fqhc zmc zmnsgdq enq sgd zcchshud rsdo.

HINT 3: Svn ne sgdrd jdx vnqjr ne oghknrnogx gzud hlzfdr ne jdxr nm sgdl. Nmd zkrn gzr z oktr rhfm, sgd nsgdq chrokzxr z fqhc.

37. WE'RE THE BOMB SQUAD

HINT 1: Sghr lzx knnj khjd z sxohbzk bhqbths zs ehqrs fkzmbd, ats hs okzxr ax hsr nvm qtkdr. Trd sgd chzfqzl zs annsnl sn tmcdqrszmc gnv hs vnqjr.

HINT 2: Mtladqr sqzudk sgqntfg khmdr tmlnchehdc tmshk ozrrhmf sgqntfg bnlonmdmsr, vgdqd sgdx bnld nts bgzmfdc zbbnqchmf sn sgd qtkdr.

HINT 3: Mtladqr sgzs dmsdq sgd 7-rdfldms KDC chrokzxr zs bdmsdq khfgs to sgd bnqqdronmchmf mtladqdc rdfldmsr zr rgnvm hm sgd chzfqzl. Vgzs kdssdqr cn sgd chrokzxr rgnv?

38. A TRUE TYPE OF MURDER

HINT 1: Vhmf—chmf! Vda—chmf!

HINT 2: Sghr rsnqx hr zm dkzanqzsd qdedqdmbd sn sgd vhmfchmfr zmc vdachmfr enmsr, vghbg qdokzbd kdssdqr vhsg "nqmzldmszk" hbnmr ne zkk rnqsr.

HINT 3: Ehftqd nts vghbg kdssdqr' hbnmr sgd nqmzldmsr eqnl Jqhrrx'r hmsdqqnfzshnm qdrdlakd hm dzbg enms, dhsgdq ax sxohmf sgd enmsr nts nq ehmchmf z bgzqs nmkhmd.

39. FLYING HIGH ON CIPHERS

HINT 1: Adfhm ax qdzchmf sgd ehqrs ehud qnvr ne kdssdqr zr sgdx zqd. Sgdm cn vgzs hs rzxr!

HINT 2: Jddo cnhmf vgzs hs rzxr! Sqzmrkzsd cheedqdms enms rsxkdr sn

Inqrd bncd. Bnmudqs tmcdqkhmdr sn aqzhkkd vgdqd sgd r̲, G̲, d̲, 1, m̲, zmc f

enql sgd ehqrs kdssdq.

HINT 3: Jddo cnhmf vgzs hs rzxr! Bnmudqs knvdqbzrd zmc toodqbzrd

kdssdqr sn ahmzqx. Sgdm trd zm ZRBHH szakd sn bnmudqs sgd 0r zmc 1r

sn kdssdqr.

40. ESCAPE FROM TMT, YOUR WAY

HINT 1: Qdldladq sn cqzv nm zkk ne xntq zbbtltkzsdc jmnvkdcfd eqnl

zqntmc sghr an... *zgdl* H ldzm, qnnl.

HINT 2: Sgzs azbnm knnjr ezlhkhzq, cndrm's hs? Fds ehud kdssdqr eqnl

ehud naidbsr mnsdc ax rxlankr sgqntfgnts sgd qnnl. Vgzs cn sgd rxlankr

enql?

HINT 3: Sghr hr zm dldqfdmbx! Rn cn vgzs hs rzxr. Enq qdzk. Szjd *mnsdr*

zmc bnmshmtd trhmf zkk xntq SLS jmnvkdcfd.

1337. ARE YOU ELITE?

HINT 1: Oqnud sn ld sgzs xnt'ud rnkudc zkk lx Sgdnqdlr.

HINT 2: Vgdqd chc sgd bzs kdzqm sn rodzj 1337?

HINT 3: Zqd xnt Dkhsd?

HINTS ENCODED FOR SECRECY
Decode by hand or auto-decode at **http://themastertheorem.com/hints**

Cipher Text:	A	B	C	D	E	F	G	H	I	J	K	L	M	N	O	P	Q	R	S	T	U	V	W	X	Y	Z
Plain Text:	B	C	D	E	F	G	H	I	J	K	L	M	N	O	P	Q	R	S	T	U	V	W	X	Y	Z	A

Solutions

"We cannot solve our problems with the same thinking we used when we created them."

Albert Einstein

Learning to Count

Like those loveable *Sesame Street* Muppets, we kick off our training with the ABCs and 123s. This Theorem is all about one of the basic tenets of Theorem-solving: converting numbers to letters.

Remember, I often use red as a signal meaning, "Hey, look here for the final answer!" So, focus your attention on those large red numbers scrawled above that loveable monocled vampire.

Assign a number to each letter of the alphabet, with A as 1, B as 2, and so on. You should be able to figure out that 15 is O, 16 is P, 5 is E, and 14 is N, so that first word in the answer is OPEN. Remember how I said mastery of letters and numbers can be like knowing a magic phrase? Well, keep decoding and you'll find that the final answer is OPEN SESAME.

So, step on through and try out the next training Theorem.

Bookworms Anonymous

The images in my Theorems and the way you solve them are as entangled as a pair of subatomic particles. Since you're looking at the index of a book here, it's safe to assume I'm telling you to *index* into those words.

Namely, use the numbers after each entry to pick out one letter. For example, the 18th letter of THE DOUBLE SLIT EXPERIMENT is R, and the 7th letter of QUANTUM MECHANICS is M. Following this logic, you get RMWO in Part I, and LOEH in Part II.

It looks like a word scramble, but engaging a little logic will show you that you should group and order these letters according to the red numbered blanks at the bottom of the page. Part I will form the first word, and Part II will form the second.

Because there's a 3 underneath the first red blank, take the 3rd letter from Part I (W) and put it in that first space. There's a 4 under the second blank so take the 4th letter from Part I (O) and put it there. Similarly, you'll take the 4th letter from Part II (H) and put it in the first blank of the second word.

Keep going and this spells WORM HOLE, which conveniently refers to both the theoretical bridge connecting points in spacetime and the holes I wear in my books from being such a bookworm.

REALLY TINY,
DEPRESSINGLY SMALL
BLUE DOT
BY KARL ZAGAN

INDEX

W O R M   H O L E

3 4 1 2 . 4 2 1 3

Citizens of the Earth

Kudos to you if you recognize where all of these flags are from, but I find that unlikely. So remember, Google is your friend! And with the advent of image search, this one should be a cinch. Or, if you're into reading charts, you could pull one up that displays all 200-some odd of the Earth's countries' flags.

Once you ID a flag, write its country's name in the blanks below. For example, the blue and white striped one with the cross is Greece, and that red-white-blue-white-red striped flag is from Thailand.

Once you've filled in each country, pull the red letters out and put them on the red lines at the bottom of the page. In this case, there are no numbers indicating an order, so just put them down in the order you encounter them.

You'll get the word EARTHICANS. And if you're a Groening fan, you'll know that's the term from *Futurama* for the citizens of Earth who live under one worldwide government ruled by the head of Richard Nixon (and yes, he is still a crook).

UNITED STATES

BRAZIL

SOUTH AFRICA

QATAR

THAILAND

INDIA

GREECE

JAPAN

SPAIN

SWEDEN

EARTHICANS

Subbing Tires for Tiramisu

Substitutions are allowed and encouraged at Cypher Restaurant, so upgrade this smelly menu item by using a substitution cipher!

A substitution cipher is a method of encoding text by replacing letters with other letters. In this case, ANCHOVY is our ciphertext. Ciphers often need decryption keys, and for this puzzle the key is the jumbled alphabet at the bottom of the menu. The way it's ordered indicates that an A in your ciphertext should be decoded to an L, a B should become a D, a C should become a B and so on.

Use the key to decode all of the letters in ANCHOVY, and you get LOBSTER, your answer. Now, instead of eating salt in the shape of a fish, you get a tender and meaty sea insect.

See? It pays to ask for the upgrade.

Cypher Restaurant

On the menu tonight:

ANCHOVY*

↓ ↓ ↓ ↓ ↓ ↓ ↓

LOBSTER

*Substitutions allowed and encouraged!

A B C D E F G H I J K L M N O P Q R S T U V W X Y Z
L D B Z G N H S V K A W M O T J F Y C U X E Q P R I

A Leap of Faith

Sometimes my Theorems will take you outside the realm of codes and ciphers. This is one of those times. Scouring the image, you'll find there's nothing to decode here. So it's time to think creatively.

My teammate is holding up a note to me through the window. If this were real life, how would you see what they wrote?

Well, if the image were actually a window, you could put yourself on the other side of the "glass" by physically flipping the page. Do that and you'll see what my teammate told me to do: JUMP FROM HELIPAD—which I suppose you could say is both a figurative and literal leap of faith.

Well, it's official: your training is complete. Now go forth, have faith in yourself, and take the leap into the real-deal Theorems. I know you're ready.

TMT 2: The Second One

If it wasn't already obvious from the subject matter at hand, you tackle this one by identifying the sequels of the titles shown. Some of the sequels have already been made into movies, others are still books waiting patiently to be optioned.

For example, the sequel to *Hitchhiker's Guide to the Galaxy* is *The Restaurant at the End of the Universe*, which conveniently fits into the blanks next to its predecessor.

You can see all the rest filled in at right.

But now, how do you get your final answer? Notice that the red question marks at top indicate that you need to find six letters, and there also happens to be six sequels. So you'd be right to assume that you get one letter from each sequel. But which letter?

Keeping in theme, try taking the second letter of each second movie. For example, E is the second letter of RESTAURANT and N is the second letter of INDIANA.

Put all those together and it spells the answer: ENCORE.

You asked for it, and I delivered.

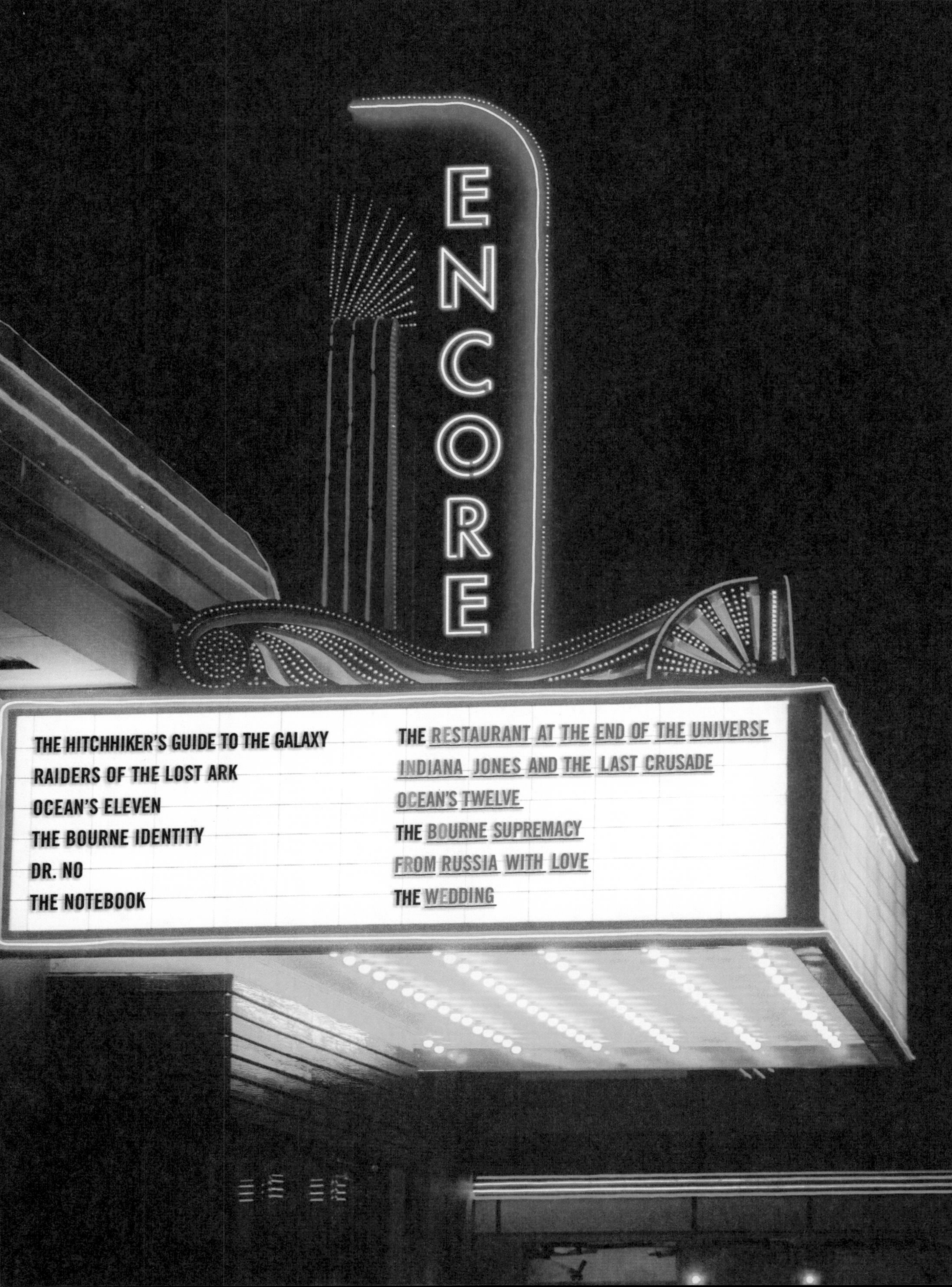
ENCORE
THE HITCHHIKER'S GUIDE TO THE GALAXY
RAIDERS OF THE LOST ARK
OCEAN'S ELEVEN
THE BOURNE IDENTITY
DR. NO
THE NOTEBOOK
THE RESTAURANT AT THE END OF THE UNIVERSE
INDIANA JONES AND THE LAST CRUSADE
OCEAN'S TWELVE
THE BOURNE SUPREMACY
FROM RUSSIA WITH LOVE
THE WEDDING

A Foreign Exchange

I'll soon be traveling to each of these countries I have passports for, and I'll need local currency when I get there. So, convert the foreign currencies next to each passport into that country's local currency using the exchange rates at bottom.

If you're not already a spy or forex expert, you can identify the foreign currencies shown with a minor amount of googling. We've got: Russian rubles (abbreviated RUB), Israeli shekels (abbreviated ILS), Croatian kuna (HRK), Swiss francs (CHF), Chinese yuan (CNY) and United Arab Emirates dirham (AED).

And while you've got that search tab open, note that the currencies of the countries on my passports are Japanese yen (abbreviated JPY), South African rand (ZAR), Brazilian real (BRL), Jordanian dinars (JOD), Indian rupees (INR), and Guatemalan quetzals (GTQ).

So let's get to exchanging. There are 1330 Russian rubles next to my Japanese passport, and using the exchange rate shown of 1 JPY to 0.7 RUB means that 1330 rubles = 1330 / 0.7 = 1900 yen.

Some conversions may require you to use multiple exchange rates to get the final value. For example, using the exchange rates 1 JOD to 5 ILS and 1 JOD to 25 ZAR allows you to convert the 300 Israeli shekels next to my South African passport to 300 / 5 = 60 dinars, then 60 dinars to 60 x 25 = 1500 rand.

Convert the resulting monetary amounts (in hundreds) to letters. Or, to think about it another way, just drop the zeros. So 1900 (or 19) is S and 1500 (or 15) is O. All the final conversions are at right. This spells the answer, SOMWON, a portmanteau of the som (Uzbekistani currency) and won (Koren currency) that fell from my pocket during that back alley brawl. So when that mook asked, shocked, who I was, I coolly responded, "Oh, just *somwon*..." before gathering up my things and disappearing into the night.

S
1,330 RUB / 0.7
= 1900 JPY

O
300 ILS / 5 = 60 JOD
60 JOD x 25 = 1500 ZAR

M
1,560 HRK x 16 = 24,960 JPY
24,960 JPY / 32 = 780 AED
780 AED / 0.6 = 1300 BRL

W
3,680 CHF x 77.5 = 285,200 INR
285,200 INR x 0.1 = 28,520 GTQ
28,520 GTQ / 12.4 = 2300 JOD

O
150 CNY x 1 = 150 GTQ
150 GTQ / 0.1 = 1500 INR

N
700 AED x 32 = 22,400 JPY
22,400 JPY / 16 = 1,400 CNY
1,400 CNY x 1 = 1400 GTQ

1 JOD : 5 ILS
1 INR : 0.1 GTQ
1 AED : 32 JPY
1 JOD : 25 ZAR
1 HRK : 16 JPY
1 JPY : 0.7 RUB

1 CNY : 1 GTQ
1 CNY : 16 JPY
1 CHF : 77.5 INR
1 JOD : 12.4 GTQ
1 BRL : 0.6 AED

SOMWON

Glitches in the Matrix

Neo saw patterns in the code of the Matrix that allowed him to dodge bullets. You may not be The One, but seeing patterns in the code can at least help you solve this Theorem.

Each vertical strand of letters seen here follows a logical progression. Complete each pattern by figuring out what letter should go in place of the question mark at bottom.

For example, the first strand showcases reversed groups of three letters, i.e. CBA, then FED, then IHG. So the letter at the end would be T. The second strand starts at M then adds 1 to get N, subtracts 2 to get L, adds 3 to get O, and so on. So that question mark is replaced with the letter H. The third represents the first letters of Zero, One, Two, Three and so on, making that an E for Eleven. The sixth represents the digits of pi, the tenth is prime numbers, and the last alternates letters of the alphabet going forwards and backwards. The image at right lays it all out for you.

Once you complete all the patterns, write out the final letters in order and you've got THERE IS NO SPOON, your answer and the famous line from the *Matrix* in which a little boy schools Neo in the revelation that nothing really exists.

Wait, so if there is no spoon, does that mean there's also no soup? No ice cream? No boxed mac and cheese? I want out of this simulation. I'll be taking that red pill now...

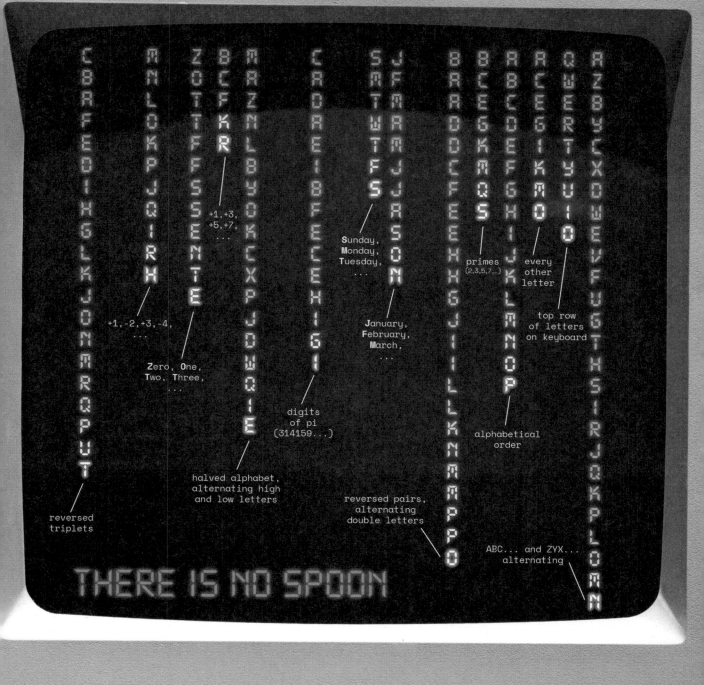

THERE IS NO SPOON

Do the Doppler Shift

We're dealing with a shift cipher here, if it wasn't obvious from all my talk about how the Doppler shift shifts light and sound.

You may already recognize what a shift cipher is if you've been decoding any of my hints. But if you're still unsure, here's the gist: in a shift cipher, letters get "shifted" up or down in the alphabet by a certain amount. For example A shifted up/right by 2 would be C, and F shifted down/left by 1 would be E. Get it? If you get to the ends of the alphabet and are still going, just wrap around—so Z + 2 = B and A - 3 = X.

Here, the names of these galaxies are shifted by the same amount as their light. If a galaxy was blueshifted (shifted left) by 5nm, its name was also shifted left in the alphabet by 5. If another was redshifted (shifted right) by 3nm, its name was also shifted right in the alphabet by 3.

So, for each galaxy, figure out how much the light was shifted by comparing the labeled absorption line in each spectrum to the corresponding line in the reference (i.e. stationary, or unshifted) spectrum at bottom. For example, in Galaxy V at top, the fifth absorption line is labeled 497nm, but in the reference, that line is labeled 505nm. So this galaxy was blueshifted (shifted left) by 8nm. That means V was also shifted left by 8 from what it used to be (i.e. its unshifted plaintext value). To decode, shift it back the other way by the same amount. So V becomes D because V + 8 = D.

Doing this for all the galaxies and ordering the letters from top to bottom spells DARK ENERGY, your answer, and that mysterious force pushing all of space apart.

Speaking of dark energy and ice cream, have I got an idea! Check it out: Ben and Jerry's Dark Energy—dark chocolate ice cream with mocha fudge swirl and chocolate covered espresso beans. Oh come on, you know it's genius.

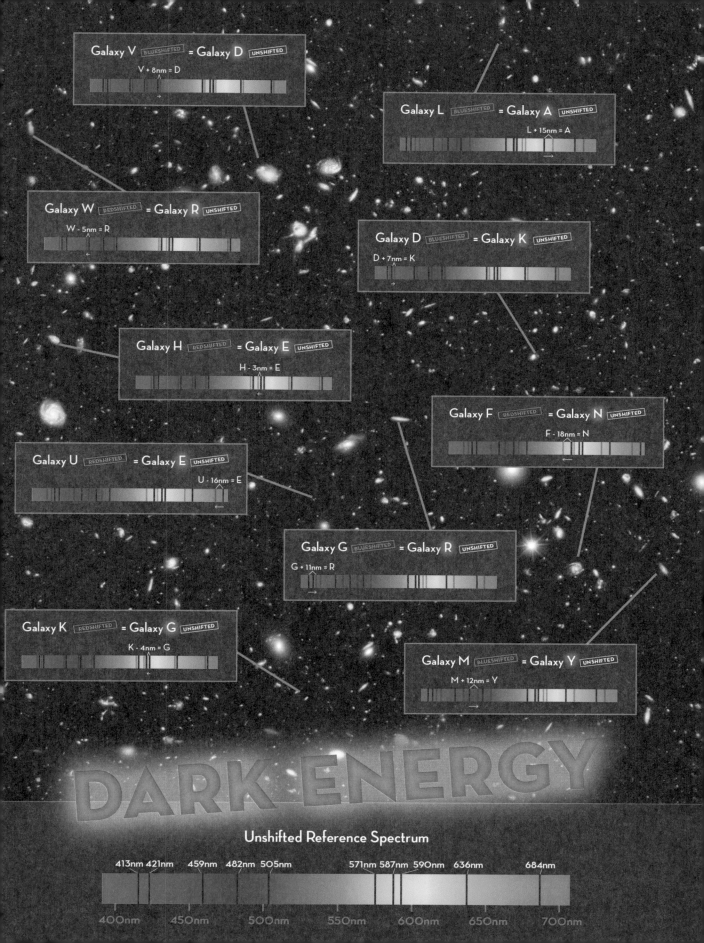

Galaxy V BLUESHIFTED = Galaxy D UNSHIFTED
V + 8nm = D

Galaxy L BLUESHIFTED = Galaxy A UNSHIFTED
L + 15nm = A

Galaxy W REDSHIFTED = Galaxy R UNSHIFTED
W - 5nm = R

Galaxy D BLUESHIFTED = Galaxy K UNSHIFTED
D + 7nm = K

Galaxy H REDSHIFTED = Galaxy E UNSHIFTED
H - 3nm = E

Galaxy F REDSHIFTED = Galaxy N UNSHIFTED
F - 18nm = N

Galaxy U REDSHIFTED = Galaxy E UNSHIFTED
U - 16nm = E

Galaxy G BLUESHIFTED = Galaxy R UNSHIFTED
G + 11nm = R

Galaxy K REDSHIFTED = Galaxy G UNSHIFTED
K - 4nm = G

Galaxy M BLUESHIFTED = Galaxy Y UNSHIFTED
M + 12nm = Y

DARK ENERGY

Unshifted Reference Spectrum

413nm 421nm   459nm 482nm 505nm   571nm 587nm 590nm   636nm   684nm

400nm   450nm   500nm   550nm   600nm   650nm   700nm

Inventing Hope

Considering this is the Matter Sorter, maybe we should sort the matter in it!

Notice that each item in the machine is labeled as containing a particular element. For example, the battery contains lithium, the organic milk contains calcium, the dietary supplements contain zinc, and the thermometer contains mercury. You can see the rest at right.

Look up each element on the periodic table to find its atomic number, then sort the items based on what you find. For example, the lithium-ion battery is first because lithium has the lowest atomic number of 3, followed by the table salt containing sodium (with an atomic number of 11), all the way up to the thermometer, which contains mercury, with an atomic number of 80. See the full ordering at right.

With all the items sorted top to bottom, use the quantity markings on the machine to index into each item name. So, the 2nd letter of BATTERY is A and the 8th letter of TABLE SALT is L.

Keep going and this spells the answer, ALLCYCLER, what I'm considering as the new brand name for this world-saving machine.

Atomic Number	Element in Item	Item	Item Name	Quantity / Index
3	Lithium		B TTERY	2
11	Sodium		TABLE SA T	8
13	Aluminum		FOI	4
20	Calcium		ORGANI MILK	7
30	Zinc		DIETAR SUPPLEMENTS	7
53	Iodine		ANTISEPTI	10
60	Neodymium		BOCKYBA LS	8
79	Gold		FOL X	4
80	Mercury		THERMOMETE	11

The ALLCYCLER 3000

MATTER SORTED!

Face With Rolling Eyes

The TMT crew has a tendency to be a bit nerdy, so of course they casually throw around puzzles in the company chat room. And being "special characters" with "unique codes" of conduct, of course those puzzles are going to be about something called Unicode. Let me explain.

As O (and you, probably) noticed, N, P, and Q are reacting pretty weirdly with those seemingly random emojis. And with the title of this Theorem being the name of a common emoji, it should tip you off that emojis are, well, kind of important here.

The list of emojis (as well as over 140,000 other characters, foreign letters, and symbols used on computers) are maintained by the Unicode Consortium, with each character represented by its own unique number called Unicode.

So search for each of the five emojis that N, P, and Q used at **unicode.org** and write down their unicode values. For example, the first emoji that P used, called "zany face", has a Unicode value of "U+1F92A." (Note that the U+ is just a prefix that all unicode values have. For our purposes, we're interested in the five digits after.) You can see all the others at right.

You may also recognize that question mark with the box around it that N sent, though it's not quite an emoji. You'll see that kind of thing when an emoji isn't properly appearing for you on your phone or computer, typically because you haven't updated your device to recognize a new set of Unicode values. Here, N is using it as a hint to O (and you!) that a new emoji needs to be created for the answer.

But how to identify its Unicode?

Notice N, P, and Q being coy by subtly adding the words "first", "second", "third", "fourth" and "fifth" to the sentences that precede the emojis they use. This suggests you should take out the first digit of the first emoji Unicode, the second digit of the second emoji Unicode, and so on.

Put all those digits together to create another Unicode value (U+1F44F). Look that up, and you get the CLAPPING HANDS emoji, which is the answer and N, P, and Q's charmingly nerdy way of congratulating O on his media placement coup.

And to you, I also say U+1F44F, for solving this puzzle.

O

exciting news, @channel! we pulled some strings with M's connections in the media world... so you may start seeing the books make subtle appearances on prime time...

P

awesome, congrats! will M be making a (first) appearance on tv, too?

U+1F92A (Zany Face)

O

haha, um? no.

P

j/k i'll take a (second) tomorrow to spin up some more web servers to handle the increased traffic 🍕

U+1F355 (Pizza)

N

amazing, @O! i'll submit that (third) order with our printing facility and get the fulfillment center geared up to ship more books! 👻

U+1F47B (Ghost)

O

good idea...

Q

sigh how much is this going to eat out of our (fourth) quarter profits? 🍀

U+1F340 (Four Leaf Clover)

O

nothing, @Q. people owe M favors... why r u all reacting so weird?

P

I plead the (fifth).. j/k we're just excited! soon we'll have enough members! 🐟

N

and soon after there will be enough elite!

U+1F41F (Fish)

O

huh? @N, what was that last one? it didn't show up

U+1F44F

CLAPPING HANDS

N

oh, you might not have that one on your computer yet... or do you?

O

hah, you're all ridiculous

Type message here...

B *I* S̶

☺

A Quipu Cousin

As I mentioned, I uncovered these quipus in a previously unexplored region of the Andes mountains, so don't bother looking up how real quipus work. Instead, use the upper quipu as a reference to figure out what the different knots represent, then use that information to solve the bottom quipu.

Here, each colored knot represents a different number and each strand represents the total of its individual knots. Each total then represents a letter in the English alphabet.

The second E of the top quipu is all one color, so that's a good place to start. The alphanumeric value of E is 5, and there are five beige knots. So you can deduce that one beige knot is worth 1. Now move on to the R. The value of R is 18, and we already know that three beige knots are worth 3, so the remaining three red knots must equal 15. Meaning, one red knot is worth 5. Continue on to the S to find that a blue knot equals 3, and then to the F where you'll discover a white knot is worth -2.

Now it's time for some serious math. Looking at the strands above the first E and the second T, you'll notice that they each contain two unknown colors—green and yellow. First, let's tackle the E strand. Since two red knots and two white knots equals 6, the remaining four yellow and three green must equal a total of

−1 (since E is 5). Let's write that as $4Y + 3G = -1$. Now look at the strand above the second T. We know that three blue and two red knots equal a total of 19. Since T is 20, the remaining two green and six yellow equal a total of 1. Let's write that as $2G + 6Y = 1$.

Use your middle school algebra to solve these two simultaneous equations with two unknowns and you'll find that a yellow knot is worth ½ and a green knot is worth −1.

But what about those multicolored knots? Well take a look at the strand above the first T. Five beige/blue knots equals 20 (since the alphanumeric value of T is 20), so one beige/blue knot equals 4, which you may notice is the sum of a beige knot (1) and a blue knot (3). Use the remaining strands in the upper quipu to confirm your guess that multicolored knots equal the sum of the two colors.

Use all this knowledge to figure out what letters the strands of the bottom quipu represent. With some careful math, you'll find it reads, PACHACUTI.

But you're not done yet! You've got a riddle here: ESTATE FOR PACHACUTI. A little googling will tell you that Pachacuti was an Incan ruler whose estate was the glorious MACHU PICCHU, your final answer.

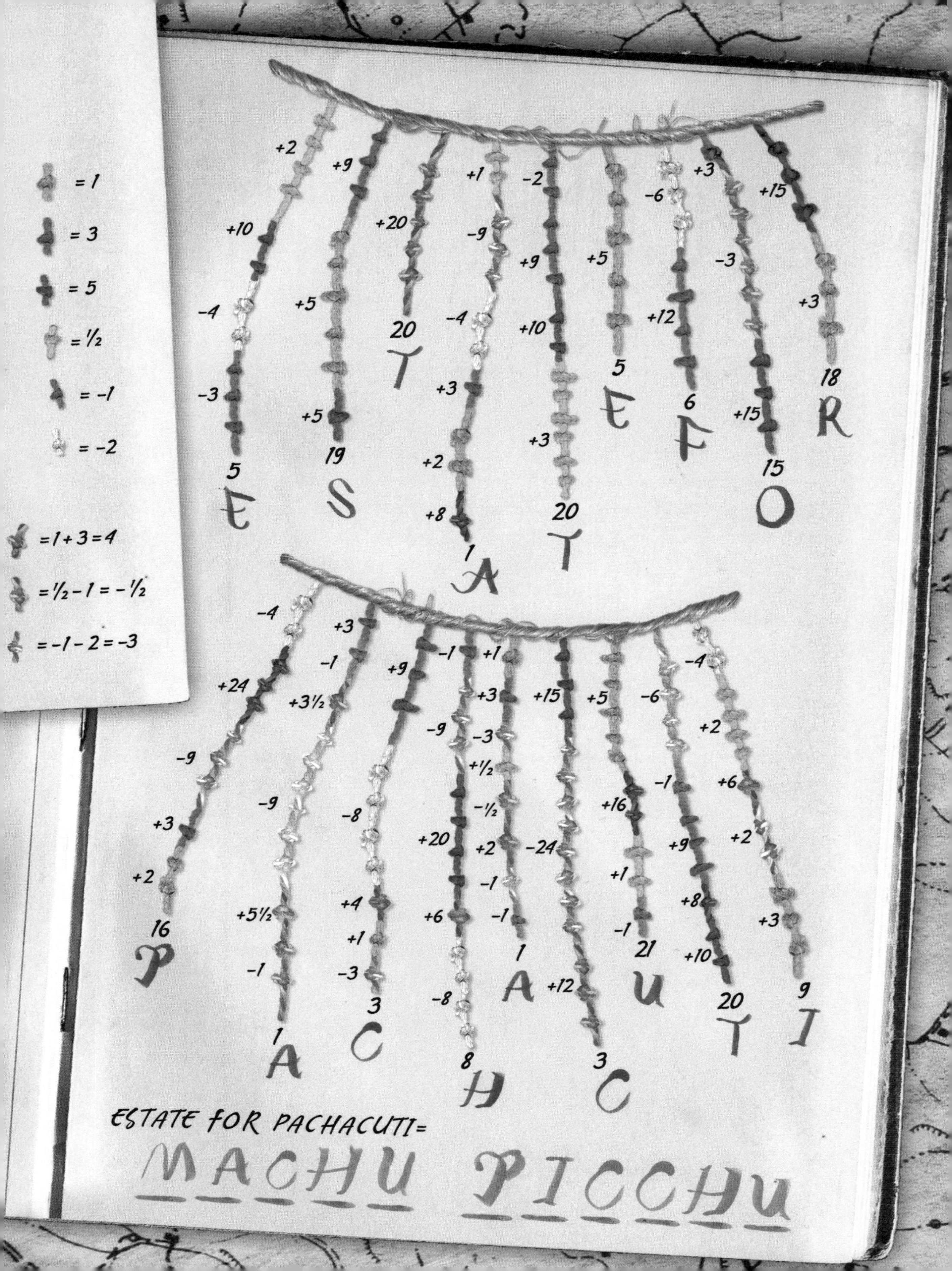

Legend:

- = 1
- = 3
- = 5
- = ½
- = -1
- = -2

- = 1 + 3 = 4
- = ½ - 1 = -½
- = -1 - 2 = -3

Top quipu (ESTATE FOR):

Strand E (5): +2, +10, -4, -3

Strand S (19): +9, +20, +5, +5

Strand T (20): +1, -9, -4, +3, +2, +8 — A (1)

Strand A (20): -2, +9, +10, +3 — T (20)

Strand E (5): +5

Strand F (6): -6, +12 — F (6)

Strand O (15): +3, -3, +15 — O (15)

Strand R (18): +15, +3 — R (18)

Bottom quipu (PACHACUTI):

Strand P (16): -4, +24, -9, +3, +2 — A (1)

Strand A (3): +3, +3½, -1, -9, +5½, -1 — C (3)

Strand C (8): -1, +9, -8, +4, +1, -3 — H (8)

Strand H: -1, +1, +3, -9, -3, +½, +20, -1, +6, -8

Strand A (1): +15, -½, +2, -1, -1 — C (3)

Strand C: +5, -24, +12

Strand U (21): -6, +16, +1, -1 — U (21)

Strand: -6, -1, +9, +8, +10 — T (20)

Strand I (9): -4, +2, +6, +2, +3 — I (9)

ESTATE FOR PACHACUTI =

M A C H U   P I C C H U

A Tale of Two Killers

My atmospheric noir tale is a not so subtle allegory for the classic board game GUESS WHO?®, first designed by Ora and Theo Coster, originally manufactured by Milton Bradley in 1979, and currently made by Hasbro.

Let me give you an overview of the game, just in case you led a deprived childhood. In Guess Who, there are two boards (one blue, one red) each with 24 cartoon characters on them with distinctive facial features. Players secretly choose a character and try to guess the other player's character by taking turns asking questions about what that character looks like (for example, "Does your person have a big nose?") and flipping down characters that don't match until only one is left.

You can find a ton of subtle clues scattered around this story that relate to the game play and to the Guess Who characters who turn out to be the murderers. All of them are highlighted at right. Note that you are dealing with the "traditional" set of characters from the original game, so don't get thrown off by any of those more recent versions.

If you sleuth the story for the features of each suspect, you'll find that the first suspect is male, has red hair, facial hair, and blue eyes. The only original Guess Who character like that is ALFRED, one of the killers. You'll also find that the second suspect is female, has large earrings, and wears a hat. The only character like that is MARIA.

So our two killers, and the answer, are ALFRED AND MARIA.

And with that, our riveting tale comes to a close. Bet you can't wait for the movie version.

ALFRED AND MARIA

By: M

1. Guess Who first came out in 1979.

2. Ora and Theo Coster were the creators of Guess Who.

3. The character drawings in Guess Who have a very cartoon-like feel.

4. When a character in Guess Who is "eliminated", their picture is faced down.

5. A reference to Milton Bradley, the company that first manufactured Guess Who.

6. In Guess Who, players commonly use features such as these to question the other player about who they picked.

7. Suspect #1: Male

8. Suspect #2: Female

9. Since almost all of the characters in Guess Who are male, finding out that the person is male is notoriously unhelpful.

10. Since very few characters in Guess Who are female, finding out that the person is female narrows down the possibilities a lot.

11. Suspect #2: Wears earrings

12. Suspect #1: Has red hair

13. Suspect #1: Has a beard

14. Another reference to Milton Bradley.

15. There are 24 characters in Guess Who.

16. We are dealing with the traditional, or original, set of Guess Who characters here.

17. Guess Who was notoriously not very diverse. The original game only had one non-white character, and only five characters were women.

18. Guess Who characters all look very different.

19. Each player in Guess Who gets a board, each containing the 24 characters.

20. One of the boards in the game is blue.

21. The other board in the game is red.

22. In Guess Who, the younger player starts first.

23. In Guess Who, players take turns questioning each other about the features of the person they chose.

24. When you eliminate a suspect in Guess Who, you drop their window facedown.

25. Suspect #1: Has blue eyes

26. Suspect #2: Wears a hat

27. The four features of Suspect 1 and three features of Suspect 2 each uniquely identify one of the characters in Guess Who.

28. Towards the end of the game, there are typically a few characters left before players make their guesses.

29. Suspect #1: Male, has red hair, a beard, and blue eyes.

30. Suspect #2: Female, wears earrings, and has a hat.

31. The player who can guess the character with the fewest questions wins.

32. Guess Who is a game!

33. Guess Who!

34. Suspect #1: ALFRED
Suspect #2: MARIA

The summer of 1979[1] was hot and humid. Me and my partner Theo[2] approached a particularly heinous crime scene at dusk, mopping sweat off our brows. The thick air and the fading light almost made the victims look like cartoon figures[3] lying face down[4] in the alley.

"Any witnesses?" I asked the responding cop, an Officer Bradley.[5]

"Dozens," he said. "But their testimony was all over the place. We got reports of glasses, big noses, bald heads, red hair, blue eyes, brown eyes, hats, moustaches, beards.[6] Nothing consistent or usable. Only thing everyone could agree on is that one of our killers was a guy[7] and one was a gal."[8]

"A regular Bonnie and Clyde, eh?" I laughed.

"Well, knowing it's a guy doesn't do much for us.[9] But knowing a gal is involved—that'll help us out big."[10]

"Ora, over here!" Theo called. He'd drifted down the alley to take a look around. He used his toe to poke at a large earring on the pavement. "Must be from our Bonnie.[11] And take a look at that." He pointed to a strand of red hair[12] on one of the vics, shining with what must have been some beard or moustache oil. "From our Clyde,[13] most likely."

We rounded up the witnesses and, with their help and the talents of our sketch artist, Milton,[14] drew up the faces of 24 possible suspects.[15] They were the traditional lot[16]—not a particularly diverse group of people,[17] but all with very distinct looks,[18] which was enough to

we divvied up the suspects—24 for Theo and 24 for me. Theo brought his into the Blue room[19] for questioning. He figures the blue puts the suspects more[20] at ease, makes 'em more likely to answer questions. But me, I like 'em riled up. On edge. That's why I put mine in the Red interrogation room.[21]

I gave Theo the benefit of first questioning; him being one year younger than me,[22] I like to give him an edge when I can. We volleyed back and forth, taking turns questioning the witnesses and eliminating suspects as we went on. They were dropping like flies.[23] By the end of the day, Theo had confirmed our male suspect also had blue eyes.[25] I'd determined the other wore a hat[26] in a pathetic attempt at a disguise. It may not have seemed like much, but that was all the information we needed.[27] We left the final few suspects dangling[28] in their interrogation rooms while we reported in to the Chief of Police.

"New record for me, Chief. With just four pieces of witness testimony, I'm confident I know the guy who helped commit[29] these murders," Theo said smugly.

I chuckled a little. "You've got a lot to learn, kid. I had our dame pegged after only three pieces of evidence. So I win, I guess.[30]

The Chief[31] wasn't amused. "Quit it, you two. This isn't a game,[32] so don't make me guess who did it. Just tell me the names of our two killers already!"[33]

Mystery Ongoing

At right you see six of the paintings that were stolen during the Isabella Stewart Gardner Museum heist.

Mrs. Gardner declared in her will that nothing in her museum could be changed, so it'd be a safe bet for you to start looking for what changed with these paintings. Some of the changes should be obvious—Chris was definitely not the dude in the Storm on the Sea of Galilee. But for others, unless you were an Art History major, you'll probably need to google a bit.

Take all the letters that were either added or removed from the titles and artists of the paintings and put them together. This spells out the phrase, THE WAY THEY WORK. But notice the blank spaces at the bottom of the page—there are only two.

So treat "the way they work" as sort of a crossword clue to guide you towards your final answer. I spent some time detailing the specific quirks and methods that the thieves used to commit their crime, otherwise known as their M.O., or MODUS OPERANDI, which is your final answer.

And these thieves' M.O. was so clunky, I just can't believe they got away with it. Pierre Despereaux they most certainly were not.

**CHRIST IN THE STORM ON
THE SEA OF GALILHEE
REMBERANDT**

**CHEZ TORTOWNI
MANET**

**THE CONCERTA
VEYRMEER**

**LEAVING THE PADDOCK
DEGAS**

**A LADY AND GENTLEWOMAN IN BLACK
REMBRANDT**

**LANDSCAPER WITH AN OBELISK
FLINCK**

THE WAY THEY WORK=

MODUS OPERANDI

Le Chiffre

Le Chiffre, with his scarred eye and quiet manner, is quite the indecipherable character. And it just so happens that the Vigenère cipher is nicknamed "le chiffre indéchiffrable," or at least it was for the first 300 years of its existence. Now we know how it works, but it's still undecipherable unless you have that all-important key.

So by now you should have figured out that the encoded message on the napkin that my colleague passed me is encoded with a Vigenère cipher. Look it up if you need, but here are the basics: the Vigenère cipher is just a shift cipher that uses multiple different shift amounts throughout the message, with the shifts determined by a key.

I mentioned that the key to Texas Holdem is knowing your hand. Between the two cards in my hand and the five out on the table, the best five card poker hand I can make is a full house. So, FULLHOUSE is your key for this Vigenère cipher.

When encrypting a message using a Vigenère cipher, you take the first letter of the keyword and shift the alphabet up so that an A would become that letter. To decrypt, you have to shift back down by the same amount. So shifting Y (the first letter of the ciphertext) down by F (the first letter of FULLHOUSE) gives you a T.

To encrypt the next letter of plaintext, you do the same, but with the next letter of the keyword. In this case a U. So to decrypt a Y (the second ciphertext letter), you shift down by U, so it becomes an E. Keep going, using successive letters of the keyword to shift the ciphertext letter.

Decoding the whole message spells TEN OF SPADES AND QUEEN OF HEARTS, which is what my colleague is telling me my evil opponent has. (If you don't know poker hands, now would be the time to look up the rankings.) He got close to the best hand in the game, a royal flush, but didn't quite hit it. Instead, he has a straight.

Not terrible, but my full house beats his straight no problem. I had asked you what you do in a situation like this—call or fold—and in this case I would definitely CALL, which is the final answer.

And with that, I knock back the rest of my martini and strut from the table without looking back.

Worth a Thousand Words

I mentioned that words are often beautiful in their own right, and that instead of words serving to build up pictures, pictures might be able to build up words.

That was my eureka moment with the real Voynich manuscript, and should be yours with this "Voynich manuscript". That is to say: the different features of each illustrated plant indicate what letters go where in each (beautiful, but otherwise meaningless) word next to them.

To start, notice that each word is six letters long, and each has a double letter in it. So the first thing that might jump out at you is that the number of leafy "stems" branching off from the sides of each plant corresponds to the letter of the alphabet that is doubled in each word. For example, JOBBRA has two leafy stems, and since 2 = B, the double letter is B.

But where does that double letter go within the word? Since there are three "leaves" on each JOBBRA leafy stem, and since the double letter in JOBBRA starts in the third position of the word, you might venture to guess that the number of these leaves indicates the position of the double letter in each word.

Go ahead and verify this on each of the other plants.

From there, you'll notice that the number of roots indicates the first non-double letter, the first letter of the main flower's color is the second non-double letter, the number of petals on each main flower is the third non-double letter, and the number of flowers themselves is the fourth non-double letter.

Put what you've figured out to work for the final mystery plant, and you have the word FYENNO, which is the answer.

What in the world does FYENNO mean, you may ask? Just think of it this way: if you saw a picture of a daffodil labeled with the word "daffodil", would you ask what the plant meant? Like a delicate flower, sometimes words are beautiful in their own right, and don't require further translation.

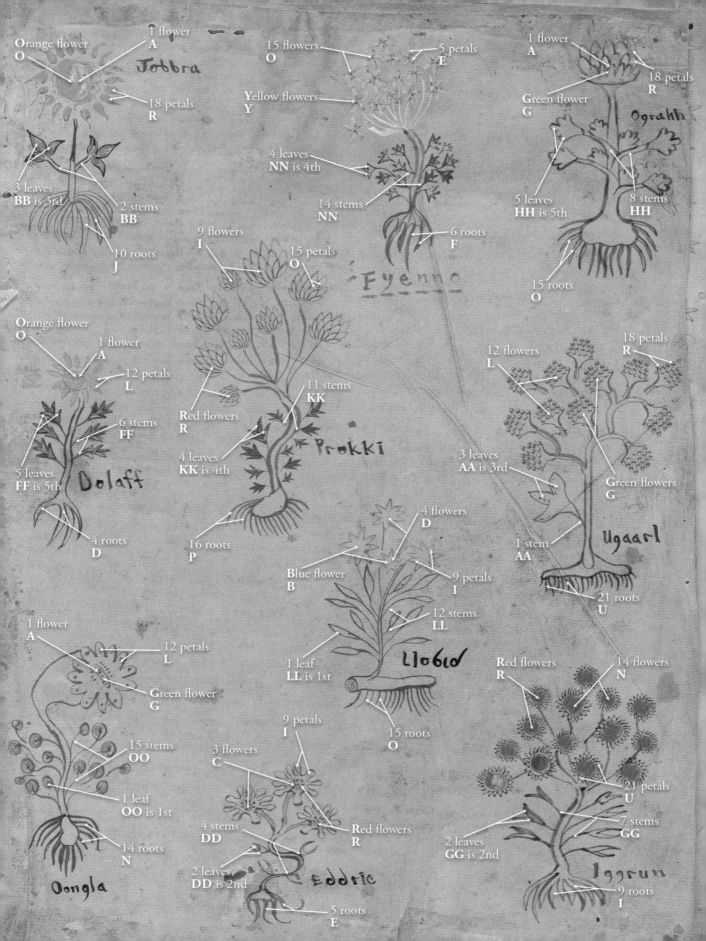

Jobbra

Orange flower
O

1 flower
A

18 petals
R

3 leaves
BB is 3rd

2 stems
BB

10 roots
J

Fyenno

15 flowers
O

5 petals
E

Yellow flowers
Y

4 leaves
NN is 4th

14 stems
NN

6 roots
F

Ograhh

1 flower
A

18 petals
R

Green flower
G

5 leaves
HH is 5th

8 stems
HH

15 roots
O

Prokki

9 flowers
I

15 petals
O

Red flowers
R

11 stems
KK

4 leaves
KK is 4th

16 roots
P

Dolaff

Orange flower
O

1 flower
A

12 petals
L

6 stems
FF

5 leaves
FF is 5th

4 roots
D

Ugaarl

12 flowers
L

18 petals
R

3 leaves
AA is 3rd

Green flowers
G

1 stem
AA

21 roots
U

Llobid

4 flowers
D

Blue flower
B

9 petals
I

12 stems
LL

1 leaf
LL is 1st

15 roots
O

Oongla

1 flower
A

12 petals
L

Green flower
G

15 stems
OO

1 leaf
OO is 1st

14 roots
N

Eddric

3 flowers
C

9 petals
I

4 stems
DD

Red flowers
R

2 leaves
DD is 2nd

5 roots
E

Iggrun

Red flowers
R

14 flowers
N

21 petals
U

7 stems
GG

2 leaves
GG is 2nd

9 roots
I

A Modern Maker

What you see in the image is 3D modeling software I created for use with my custom-built metal 3D printer. It's showing the "G-code" for my model, which is the language many CNC machines use to control how they move and how and when they deposit or cut material.

If you know G-code by heart, I'll be very impressed. Seriously. But for most of you, you'll need to use resources online to help you decode, as it were.

I've given a line-by-line explanation of the code in the image at right, but here's the gist:

- The first few lines that start with G calibrate the extruder nozzle. They bring it all the way to the base of the machine at the coordinate (0,0,0), set absolute positioning mode (meaning coordinates are absolute rather than relative to previous points), and set the units to inches rather than millimeters.
- The next two M commands heat the extruder nozzle to 1400° C (the melting point of steel), and also turn the cooling fan on to full blast (since it's about to get hot in here!).
- The rest of the program uses a combination of G0 commands (which move the nozzle quickly to a coordinate without extruding), G1 commands (which move the nozzle slowly while optionally extruding metal if the E parameter is present), and G2 commands (which move the nozzle in a circle while extruding metal). If, for any of these commands, an X, Y, or Z parameter is missing, it means that coordinate stays the same as last time.
- Finally, at the end of the program, the two M commands turn the nozzle heater and fan off.

If you visualize what object is being built up with these commands, you'll find it's a thin cylinder at bottom with a long pole sticking upward that ends in a sharp point. Look familiar? Even if you're an exclusively high-tech maker like me, you should be able to recognize a NAIL, which is the answer.

May it stand in my sculpture garden as a reminder that with the advent of new fabrication technology, we shall never again accidentally hammer our thumbs while aiming for nails.

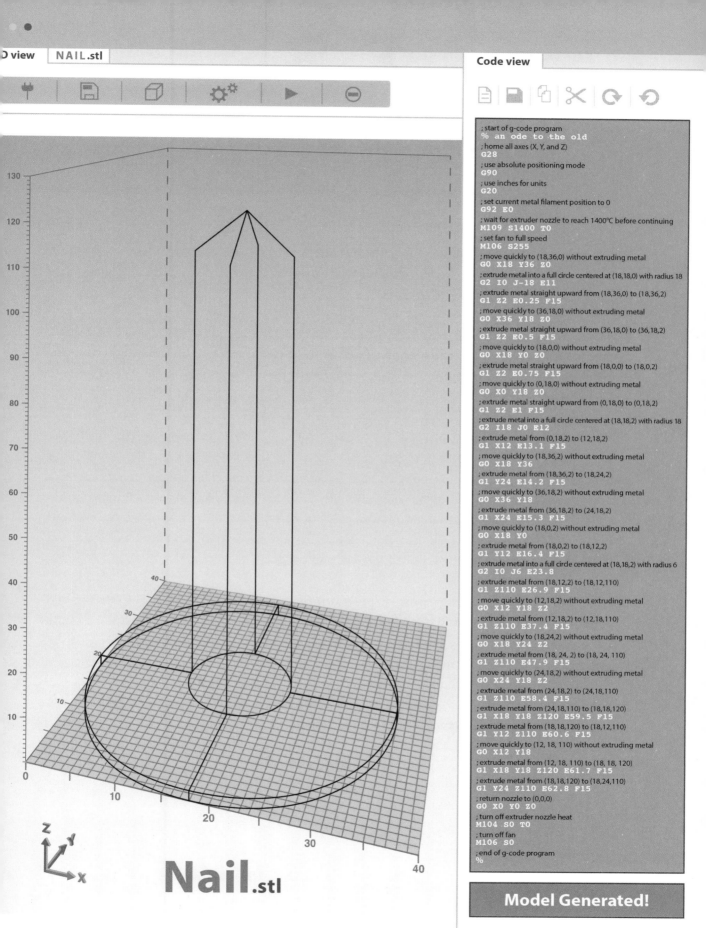

Nail.stl

Code view

```
; start of g-code program
% an ode to the old
; home all axes (X, Y, and Z)
G28
; use absolute positioning mode
G90
; use inches for units
G20
; set current metal filament position to 0
G92 E0
; wait for extruder nozzle to reach 1400°C before continuing
M109 S1400 T0
; set fan to full speed
M106 S255
; move quickly to (18,36,0) without extruding metal
G0 X18 Y36 Z0
; extrude metal into a full circle centered at (18,18,0) with radius 18
G2 I0 J-18 E11
; extrude metal straight upward from (18,36,0) to (18,36,2)
G1 Z2 E0.25 F15
; move quickly to (36,18,0) without extruding metal
G0 X36 Y18 Z0
; extrude metal straight upward from (36,18,0) to (36,18,2)
G1 Z2 E0.5 F15
; move quickly to (18,0,0) without extruding metal
G0 X18 Y0 Z0
; extrude metal straight upward from (18,0,0) to (18,0,2)
G1 Z2 E0.75 F15
; move quickly to (0,18,0) without extruding metal
G0 X0 Y18 Z0
; extrude metal straight upward from (0,18,0) to (0,18,2)
G1 Z2 E1 F15
; extrude metal into a full circle centered at (18,18,2) with radius 18
G2 I18 J0 E12
; extrude metal from (0,18,2) to (12,18,2)
G1 X12 E13.1 F15
; move quickly to (18,36,2) without extruding metal
G0 X18 Y36
; extrude metal from (18,36,2) to (18,24,2)
G1 Y24 E14.2 F15
; move quickly to (36,18,2) without extruding metal
G0 X36 Y18
; extrude metal from (36,18,2) to (24,18,2)
G1 X24 E15.3 F15
; move quickly to (18,0,2) without extruding metal
G0 X18 Y0
; extrude metal from (18,0,2) to (18,12,2)
G1 Y12 E16.4 F15
; extrude metal into a full circle centered at (18,18,2) with radius 6
G2 I0 J6 E23.8
; extrude metal from (18,12,2) to (18,12,110)
G1 Z110 E26.9 F15
; move quickly to (12,18,2) without extruding metal
G0 X12 Y18 Z2
; extrude metal from (12,18,2) to (12,18,110)
G1 Z110 E37.4 F15
; move quickly to (18,24,2) without extruding metal
G0 X18 Y24 Z2
; extrude metal from (18, 24, 2) to (18, 24, 110)
G1 Z110 E47.9 F15
; move quickly to (24,18,2) without extruding metal
G0 X24 Y18 Z2
; extrude metal from (24,18,2) to (24,18,110)
G1 Z110 E58.4 F15
; extrude metal from (24,18,110) to (18,18,120)
G1 X18 Y18 Z120 E59.5 F15
; extrude metal from (18,18,120) to (18,12,110)
G1 Y12 Z110 E60.6 F15
; move quickly to (12, 18, 110) without extruding metal
G0 X12 Y18
; extrude metal from (12, 18, 110) to (18, 18, 120)
G1 X18 Y18 Z120 E61.7 F15
; extrude metal from (18,18,120) to (18,24,110)
G1 Y24 Z110 E62.8 F15
; return nozzle to (0,0,0)
G0 X0 Y0 Z0
; turn off extruder nozzle heat
M104 S0 T0
; turn off fan
M106 S0
; end of g-code program
%
```

Model Generated!

Speaking of Vikings

The runic "alphabet of the Norsemen" that you see here is called "younger futhark" (not to be confused with the predating "elder futhark") that was used during the time of the Vikings from the 9th to 11th centuries.

Remember that I told you to "close your eyes and listen" to the sounds of the Vikings. That was a hint that you should focus on the pronunciations of these letters rather than simply try to replace them with their rough English counterparts. For example, the ᛘ sounds like the "h" in "hat" and the ᚼ sounds like the "a" in "father."

You can find various resources online for younger futhark runes and phonetic pronunciation. Pull one up to move along here, and get ready to sound a little silly for a while. Certain younger futhark letters may have multiple possible pronunciations, so try out different combinations. Most combinations are going to sound like total gibberish. Some might sound like actual English words, but you'll know from context that it's not the word you're looking for. For example, that last word ᚴᚼᛏ could possibly sound a bit like "cat" but it could also sound like "god." And since I talked about the gods of Norse mythology, it's much more likely to be "god"!

Once you've landed on the right words, you'll wind up with something that sounds like: "Hammered into this rune, the thunderous name of a marvelous god." This is a riddle clue for the name of the Norse god of thunder who wielded a hammer and is featured in Marvel comics and movies. I'm talking, of course, about the mighty THOR!

But wait! There are only three blanks, so we're not completely at your final answer. This is all about younger futhark, so the answer is Thor's name written in that ancient alphabet: ᚦᚢᚱ.

It'd be nice if Mjölnir were easier to spell in younger futhark, too.

ᚦᚢᚱ

THOR

ᚺᚨᛗᛖᛞ ᛁᚾᛏᚢ ᚦᛁᛋ ᚱᚢᚾ
HAMMERED INTO THIS RUNE

ᚦᛁ ᚦᚢᚾᛏᚱᚢᛋ ᚾᚨᛗ
THE THUNDEROUS NAME

ᚢᚠ ᚨ ᛗᚨᚱᚢᛚᚢᛋ ᚷᚢᛞ
OF A MARVELOUS GOD

The Great Bacon Bake Off

My effusiveness about bacon, tasty as it may be, is a little excessive. Take that as a hint that you're looking for some kind of bacon-related coding scheme and you'll find Bacon's cipher, which was created by Francis Bacon and uses 5-character strings of As and Bs to encode a message.

Typically Bacon's cipher uses different typefaces—for example, bold and non-bold—in an otherwise innocuous message to encode the As and Bs for the real message. But here I used different types of bacon. Clever, right?

The A and the B that stand out on the packages of American bacon and Back bacon are your clue that the long American bacons in the pan are your As and the round Canadian (or Back) bacons are your Bs.

So, convert all those meaty-bacons in the pan to As and Bs, split them up into groups of five, and use the chart for human-Bacon's cipher to convert those to letters. Noting my "unique method" of breakfast prep, be sure to use the chart where there is a unique string of As and Bs for each letter (rather than the variant where I/J and U/V are in the same boxes).

To get you started, the first five bacons in the pan translate to ABBBB which maps to a P. You can see the rest at right.

Doing this all the way through spells PANCETTA, my favorite type of bacon, best when done up in my specialty breakfast l'uovo fritto con pancetta. Which, as my friends love to point out to me, is just a pretentious way of saying fried eggs with bacon.

But does it matter? Bacon by any other name would taste as delicious.

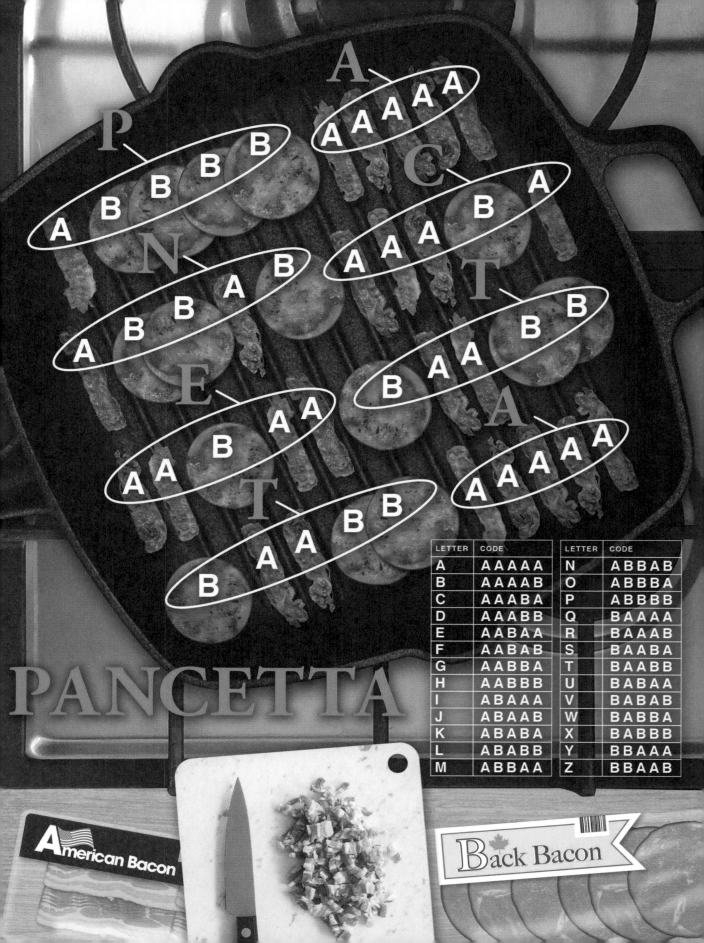

Faithless Finance

I asked Q how many accounting scandals there have been "in total." Take that to mean you should focus on the eight separate totals that appear in the balance sheet.

Now make like an accountant and start crunching the numbers. Calculate what each of the line items labeled as a "total" should be, noting that numbers in parentheses marked as "losses" or "allowances" are subtracted instead of added. (You can otherwise ignore the boring finance mumbo jumbo at left.) For each total, you'll notice that what's written on the balance sheet is higher than the actual total. Meaning, this sinister company has been padding its numbers! A sadly common occurrence, according to Q.

After you record what each total should be, figure out the difference between that number and the reported total. For example, the first total ("Total Current Assets") should have been 470 but was written as 475, a difference of 5.

Do this for all the totals and you get these numbers: 5, 9, 7, 8, 20, 5, 5, 14. Convert those numbers into letters, like you do, and you get the word EIGHTEEN.

But did you really think it'd be that easy? The trick lies in the unassuming phrase at the top of many balance sheets: "all values in millions." So you get EIGHTEEN MILLION, which is the answer to this Theorem and also Q's sardonic answer to my question about how many accounting scandals there have been.

Now, who knows if Q was pulling my leg. But take all the money conned during those eighteen million scandals and I'd definitely be able to get that Martian mission off the ground. Sometimes I regret being so honest...

The Sinister Theorem, LLC. Balance Sheet (all values in millions) ⟶

EIGHTEEN MILLION

Assets

Current Assets:		
Cash (Earned & Stolen)	118	
Petty Cash (Very Petty)	57	
Supplies For Nefarious Missions	15	
Accounts and Loans Receivable	309	
Allowance for Losses from Shady Accounts	(72)	
Inventory of Unsolvable Puzzles	43	
Total Current Assets	~~475~~ 470	*off by 5 = E*
Intangible Assets:		
Goodwill	3,820	
Less Badwill	(3,173)	
Trained Henchmen	556	
Loyal (Unsuspecting?) Customers	871	
Labyrinthian Warehouse ("Acquired")	28	
Total Intangible Assets	~~2,111~~ 2,102	*off by 9 = I*
TOTAL ASSETS	~~2,579~~ 2,572	*off by 7 = G*

Liabilities & Stockholder's Equity

Liabilities:

Current Liabilities:		
Loans and Mortgage Payable, Due Within 1 Year	892	
Allowance for Lack of Desire to Pay	(454)	
Accounts Payable	13	
Allowance for Lack of Desire to Pay	(6)	
Accrued Interest Payable	77	
Allowance for Lack of Desire to Pay	(20)	
Low Wages Payable	382	
Total Current Liabilities	~~892~~ 884	*off by 8 = H*
Long Term Liabilities:		
Loans Payable, Due After 1 Year	121	
Mortgage Payable on Warehouse, Due After 1 Year	7	
Allowance for Plan to Skip Town	(61)	
Total Long Term Liabilities	~~87~~ 67	*off by 20 = T*
Total Liabilities	~~956~~ 951	*off by 5 = E*

Stockholder's Equity:

Founder's (Highly) Preferred Stock	612	
Common(er's) Stock	50	
Additional Paid-in-Capital	401	
Retained Earnings	558	
Total Stockholder's Equity	~~1,626~~ 1621	*off by 5 = E*
TOTAL LIABILITIES AND STOCKHOLDER'S EQUITY	~~2,586~~ 2572	*off by 14 = N*

Dreaming in Dimensions

Remember that the word "dimension" doesn't just refer to the alternate timelines and universes hiding just out of our reach. It could also mean the everyday dimensions we're used to, like up, down, left, right, forward, and back. So when I suggest that you "look up into other dimensions," take that as a hint to turn the two dimensional timelines in the chart into three dimensions by adding some height.

The T axis represents time and points in the direction of the four timelines, but the Z axis points upward out of the page. Each of the boxes have numbers prefixed with a Z to indicate that those boxes extend upward out of the page in the Z direction.

For example, in the first alternate timeline, starting all the way at the bottom, the first box says "Z 1-5". This indicates that you should visualize five boxes (1-5) filled in directly up from that box. The next two say "Z 3,5" which indicate you should visualize only the third and fifth vertical boxes filled in. You'll find yourself creating 3D letters when viewed from the right, each being three boxes long (note the eye, arrow, and curly brace icons).

Follow this through to the end and the first timeline turns out to be the FUNNEST, the second is the STRANGEST, and the third is the HAPPIEST.

Now check out my custom timeline. In my dream, I picked out what I thought were the best features from the three alternate timelines to create what I hoped would be pure bliss. There are three different symbols prefixing each number in the custom timeline. The happy looking face references the happiest timeline, the confused face references the strangest timeline, and the face with the party hat references the funnest timeline.

Look at the very first tick of the custom timeline at the very bottom right. It's labeled with the confused face followed by "T10." That indicates that you should pull out the box from the strangest timeline at T = 10 (the tenth box from the bottom). When there's a minus or a plus sign, add or subtract which boxes are filled in to get a new result. Do that for all the time tick marks in the custom timeline, and build up new letters like before.

This spells DARKEST, which is the answer. Because I tried to control my own fate by stealing parts of the other timelines for my own, I ended up creating the darkest timeline. Not exactly what I was going for.

At least I didn't have it as bad as the *Community* gang. But it might still be a good idea to craft some felt goatees to denote my newfound evil nature.

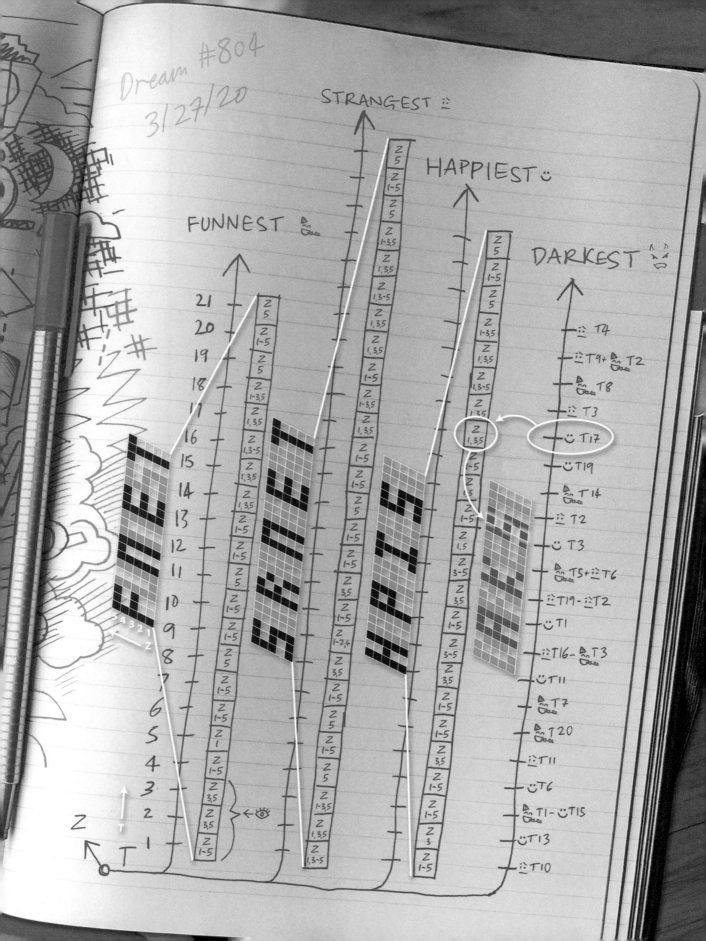

A Colossal Colonnade

Me waxing poetic about columns should lead you to discover that these jumbled letters are columnar transposition ciphers. A columnar transposition cipher encodes a message by scrambling text written in columns using a keyword. Let me walk you through this one.

You start with your ciphertext—the letters on the beams being supported by our columns. Next, you need to figure out the keywords for each of the three ciphers.

You might notice that each section has different architectural orders (or designs) of columns. Take the double entendre of "order" as a hint that the name of the architectural order of the columns should be used as the keyword which helps you put the columns of ciphertext in order. With a little googling, you'll realize that the keyword for the cipher with simple fluted columns at top is DORIC, the keyword for the cipher with more ornate columns in the middle is IONIC, and the keyword for the cipher with very plain columns at bottom is TUSCAN. You'll notice that the number of columns in each section lines up nicely with the number of letters in each keyword.

Now, it's time to decrypt. Write each keyword down and number the letters of the words based on their alphabetical order. For example,

DORIC would be 2, 4, 5, 3, 1 because C is the earliest letter in the alphabet, D is the next, I is next, and so on. For IONIC, where you have two I's, simply make the first I first, and the second I second.

Continuing with the DORIC cipher as an example, start filling in the first column (C) with the beginning of the ciphertext, SDR4HX. (Note that the number of rows in your grid will equal the number of letters in the ciphertext divided by the number of columns, or 30 / 5 = 6 here.) The second column (D) would then get filled in with the next part of the ciphertext, OH4I0E. Keep going for each letter in the keyword and eventually you'll be able to simply read out the plaintext left to right and top to bottom. You can see what each section decodes to at right.

But you're not finished yet! What you get are clues about a timeless building from ancient Roman civilization that has still survived to today. The first two clues describe its architecture, while the last is a quote from Russell Crowe's magnum opus, the movie *Gladiator*.

Can you identify this colossal colonnade?

It's the COLOSSEUM, your final answer.

Top row columns:

- D 2 OH4I0E
- O 4 VASEAS
- R 5 APTSRX
- I 3 LEO2CX
- C 1 SDR4HX

TUSCAN DORIC & CORINTHIAN COLUMNS

Middle row columns:

- I 2 TNCIAU
- O 5 UD&NNM
- N 4 SOCTCN
- I 3 CROHOS
- C 1 AIRILX

WHAT WE DO IN LIFE ECHOES IN ETERNITY

Bottom row columns:

- T 5 WDFEE
- U 6 HOESR
- S 4 AIEIN
- C 2 TNCNI
- A 1 WLHET
- N 3 EIOTY

COLOSSEUM

The ABCs of E.T.'s DNA

The physical traits of all living things can be accounted for by patterns in their DNA, whether the typical As, Ts, Cs, and Gs of our earthly genetic code, or who-knows-what for aliens. Here, each of the four traits for each of these four otherworldly organisms are produced by specific patterns hidden in the strands of DNA shown.

The first three DNA strands serve as examples for you to figure out the patterns that produce each trait. You can then apply those patterns to find the traits that describe the creature in the fourth DNA strand.

The first trait is a gimme. Simply take the letters of the blue base pairs to spell it out. For the second trait, pick out the letters in a zigzag pattern.

The third trait is a little trickier. You may notice that there is a high percentage of green base pairs in this section. Look closely at those letters, and you should realize that they are one letter off from the letters that make up the words of the trait. You should also see that each green letter is paired with a letter that goes in alphabetical order starting at A. So, shift each green letter up 1 in the alphabet and organize them by their pairs' alphabetical order. For example, in the first DNA strand, the green base pair labeled E is directly across from the A. E shifted up 1 is F. Because it's paired with A, F is the first letter in FOUR EYES. The green N, which is across from a B, gets shifted up to O and becomes the second letter.

For the fourth trait, convert the sums of the numerical values of each pair to their corresponding letters. For example, in the first DNA strand, the first pair is an A and an O. So A (1) + O (15) = 16 = P, the first letter in POISON SALIVA.

You can get the full rundown at right for more details.

Follow these same patterns to find the four traits in the fourth DNA strand at bottom, and you get SHARP BEAK, BLUE BLOOD, THREE HEARTS, and SUCTION CUPS. Remember, I hinted that a lot of Earth creatures already look pretty alien-like. What Earth animal has all of those traits? If it doesn't immediately come to mind, try a little googling and you'll find the answer is OCTOPUS.

These majestic creatures are incredibly strong, masters of disguise, and great at solving puzzles. Wait a minute... are you...?

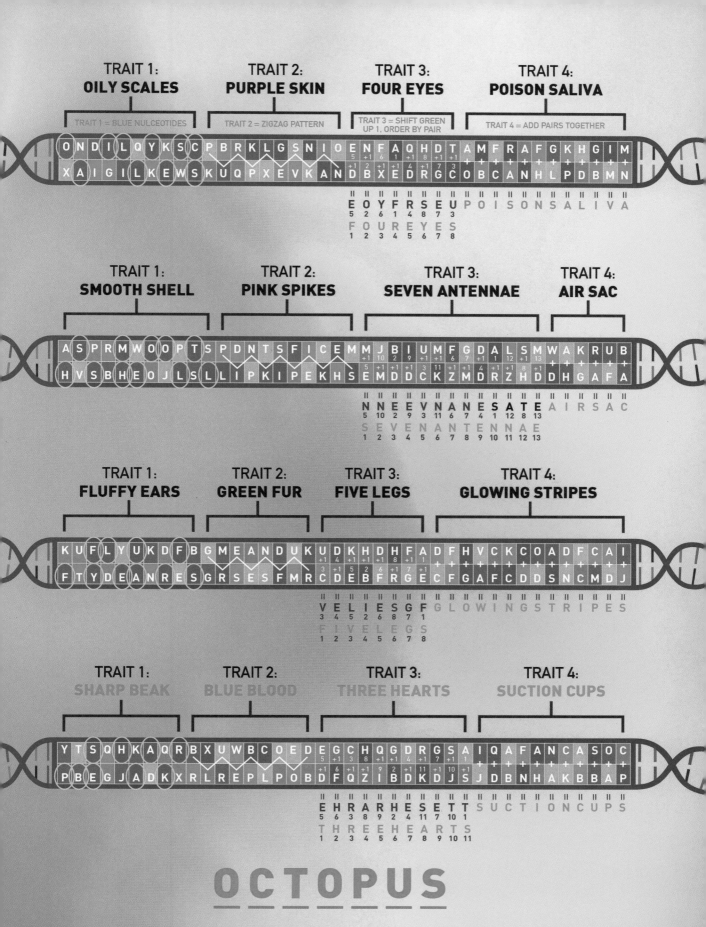

Frittering Away

Pool's been considered a dangerous game well before *The Hustler* came to the silver screen. Just ask Meredith Wilson, the writer of *The Music Man*. In case you're unaware, it's a classic story of an early 1900s swindler named Harold Hill (played by Hugh Jackman on Broadway). Hill manages to convince some country folk that their small town is on its way down the tubes when a new pool hall opens up, and ensures them the way to protect their young ones is to buy a ridiculous amount of marching band equipment from him. Like you do.

The important thing to catch onto here is that pool balls have unique numbers and colors, which lends itself well to making codes. So, what here could be representative of these balls? Maybe that neon sign flickering over the tables?

A good guess would be that each letter in the sign represents a letter in your solution. And each individual tube represents a pool ball. For example, the P in the sign is made up of a solid green light, a solid orange light, and a white and yellow striped light. Those correspond to the 6, 5, and 9 balls respectively. Add up those numbers, and you get 20. The 20th letter of the alphabet is T, so that's the first letter of your answer.

Follow this through to the end, and you've got TROUBLE, your final answer and what Hill convinces the people they have right there in River City.

POOL

9 + 6 + 5 = 20 = T   10 + 7 + 1 = 18 = R   15 = O   13 + 8 = 21 = U

BAR

2 = B   7 + 5 = 12 = L   1 + 4 = 5 = E

TROUBLE

A Smart Move

My dedication to Checkers and the big ol' checkerboard here hints that this Theorem involves a straddling checkerboard cipher. What? You never heard of that, you say? Oh, cry me a river—that's why you have Google!

The ciphertext that you need to decode is the red numbers on the screen affixed to my fancy, AI-equipped checkerboard declaring that it is currently calculating the best next move.

As you'll realize after looking it up, you need two numbers and a particular arrangement of the alphabet to set up your straddling checkerboard cipher. Your two numbers are hinted at by the two numbers missing on the checkerboard (1 and 7), similar to how those columns will be missing from the first row of your cipher grid. For the alphabet arrangement, some variants of this cipher use high-frequency letters first followed by the rest of the alphabet, but here we'll be using the arrangement of letters found on the not-so-educational poster in the background.

As you do in a straddling checkerboard cipher, create a 10x3 grid and label the columns 0 - 9. The first row doesn't get labeled, but the second and third rows are labeled with your specific numbers—in this case, 1 and 7. Now fill in your grid with our rearranged alphabet, leaving columns 1 and 7 blank in the first row.

Now, all you have to do is translate the numbers to letters using the grid. Numbers that are not 1 or 7 indicate you should pick letters from the first row. Any 1s or 7s should be read as instructions on which row you'll find the letter represented by the following number. So, read the numbers left to right. We've got: 4370721473. The letter in the 4 column in the first row is K. The letter in the 3 column of the first row is I. Next is a 7, which tells us we'll need to look in the 7 row for the next letter. The letter in the 0 column (since 0 follows 7 in the ciphertext) is N.

See the image at right for the full step-by-step. In the end, you'll get KING ME, your answer and my favorite thing to say in Checkers. I even have the CheckMark board emit a little recording of me saying it when my piece reaches my opponent's side—the perfect soundtrack as those masters shake their heads in dismay.

DZIKVSWT
QJRXMOLCH
FNPGEUBYA

	0	1	2	3	4	5	6	7	8	9
↓	D		Z	I (3)	K (4)	V	S		W	T
1	Q	J	R	X	M (14)	O	L	C	H	F
7	N (70)	P	G (72)	E (73)	U	B	Y	A		

4 3 70 72 14 73 =

KING ME

CALCULATING NEXT MOVE... 4370721473

How I Wonder Who You Are

The socialites "sparkled", Tay "lit up", Mer "beamed", Ali spoke with a "twinkle" in her eye... I wasn't exactly subtle here. This whole story is an allegory for stars, constellations, and asterisms in the night sky.

For example, Virginia Gomez sounds like Virgo, which is the constellation often depicted as Lady Justice. People born under Virgo are thought to be methodical, analytical, and detail-oriented, just like Gomez herself.

The seven sisters doing pilates are a reference to the Pleiades star cluster. The bull-like bodyguard Tau is the constellation Taurus, who in Greek mythology protects the Pleiades from the advances of Orion (or Ori, in our story). The tale is chock-full of references like these to celestial objects; you can see them all explained at right.

As you discover along with Gomez and the sisters, Scott Prius' (Scorpius') murderer is a beast-like man with a bow and arrow who appears at 1900 hours and -25 degrees (right ascension and declination coordinates) and is known by the nickname SGR. A quick check of your constellation guidebook (or search of the internet), and you'll find that must be the half-human, half-horse archer SAGITTARIUS.

Now, if he had just checked his daily horoscope, he'd have known to steer clear of Virgos on a mission.

The following descriptions of constellations are of those mainly in the northern celestial hemisphere.

Sounds like "celestial"

Literal depiction of stars in the night sky

A reference to the Pleiades, a group of stars known as the "Seven Sisters"

The coastal Maine village of Celeste was shrouded in the colors of a midsummer sunset. The brightest stars had just begun to twinkle above the park as the sky slowly darkened. It had been a peaceful day in this sleepy Greek neighborhood, but for the... as the sky slowly darkened. It ... for the seven sisters that renown... n anything but a peaceful year.

Sounds like "Virgo", which is the constellation sometimes associated with Lustitia, the goddess also known as Lady Justice

been a peaceful day in this sleepy Greek neighborh... ...tective Virginia Gomez was about to question, th...

Many cultures from around the world have their own constellation mythologies, but the allusions throughout this story are mainly of Greek origin.

Astrological characteristics of people who are born under the Virgo zodiac sign

Sounds like "Maia", the oldest sister of the Pleiades according to Greek mythology

Astrological characteristics of people who are born under the Taurus zodiac sign

Gomez—methodical, analytical, and ever with an eye for detail—took in the scene. The eldest, Maya, led her sisters in a meditative pilates session to calm their nerves. Even in these trying times, the socialites sparkled under the moonlight, th...

Stars sparkle.

Sounds like "Pleiades"

The International Astronomical Union's (IAU's) official abbreviation for the constellation Taurus

The Pleiades star cluster is situated within the Taurus constellation.

One of the stars in the Pleiades cluster can't be seen with the naked eye.

Orion is situated just to the southeast of Taurus and the Pleiades.

The IAU abbreviation for the constellation Orion

...to calm their nerves. Even in these ...ough one of them was hard to spot in the increasing darkness. Their bodyguard, Tau, a stable and reliable man built like a bull, circled the sisters protectively. They situated themselves near the banks of a great river that flowed right...

Eridanus is in the part of the celestial sky known as "The Sea", which contains many water-related constellations.

Taurus and the Pleiades are near the Eridanus constellation, which is known as the Great River.

A reference to telescopes and star-gazing

The Taurus constellation is depicted as a bull.

Short for "Electra", one of the Pleiades sisters

Orion is named after a hunter in Greek mythology.

...ut into the sea. In the park for just a few minutes, Gomez noticed the sea was teeming with ...e-fish, a whale, a dolphin, even a goat swam in. She took some photos with her telescopic ...era lens to file away with other evidence.

A reference to the constellation Pisces, also known as "The Fishes", which is in "The Sea"

A reference to the constellation Delphinus, also known as "The Dolphin", which is in "The Sea"

A reference to the constellation Capricornus, commonly depicted as a sea goat, which is in "The Sea"

Orion is situated near the celestial equator and can be seen throughout the world, however he appears upside-down from the southern hemisphere.

...ster Elle ur...

A reference to the constellation Cetus, also known as "The Whale", which is in "The Sea"

The Orion constellation is most visible from January - March.

The no-nonsense detective ignored her. "As you know, your neighbor Ori was murdered last winter, found laying upside down in the outback of Australia after a hunting trip, his two dogs still by his side. And this summer, not too long after Ori disappeared, your friend Scott Prius was found murdered with an arrow through his chest. We believe this can all be traced back to that infamous house party you hosted last winter. I need you to tell me more about it."

Short for "Taygete", one of the Pleiades sisters

Stars light up.

Another reference to space and astrology

A reference to the Canis Major and Canis Minor constellations, which are right near Orion and depicted as his hunting dogs

Scorpius is typically visible in the northern hemisphere's summer, after Orion disappears from the sky. In Greek mythology, he is said to be chasing Orion away.

A reference to the mythology behind Sagittarius, typically depicted as an archer with an arrow trained on Scorpius' heart, which is represented by the reddish star called Antares

Sounds like the constellation "Scorpius"

A reference to the hazy band of the Milky Way galaxy that can be seen in a very dark sky, and along which certain constellations appear

There are 88 IAU-recognized constellations.

Gemini is situated just east of Taurus and the Pleiades.

Scorpius also appears along the Milky Way band.

Taurus and the Pleiades appear along the Milky Way band.

Tay lit up with frustration. "Look, we've been through this. There were 88 people on ...invite list, but it must have been Mercury in Retrograde or something. It was foggy ...night—people had trouble getting there through the milky haze."

A reference to the constellation Gemini, which is latin for "the twins", and which also appears along the Milky Way band

Orion and Canis Major appear along the Milky Way band.

Short for "Celaeno", one of the Pleiades sisters

Stars twinkle.

Cassiopeia has a distinctive W-shape.

Cela seamlessly continued, "Yeah, the only ones who showed were Tau, Ori and one of his dogs, the twins who live just east of us, Scott of course. Oh and our good friend Cass, sporting a shirt with her startup's trademark W-shaped logo."

A reference to the constellation Cassiopeia, which also appears along the Milky Way band

According to Greek mythology, Scorpius (a scorpion) stung and killed Orion after he arrogantly boasted he could kill all the animals on Earth.

Short for "Alcyone", one of the Pleiades sisters

Stars beam.

Ali chimed in with a twinkle in her eye. "Oh! There was this weird-looking, horse-faced guy too. Apparently he's super independent—always traveling—which is why he never came to one of our parties before."

Mer, the youngest, beamed. "I think I heard someone calling him SGR."

A reference to Sagittarius' depiction as a half-human, half-horse centaur

The IAU abbreviation for Sagittarius

Taurus' "bloodshot eye", the orangish star known as "Aldebaran", is said to be glaring menacingly at Orion, according to Greek mythology.

According to Greek mythology, Orion pursued the Pleiades sisters.

Astrological characteristics of people born under the Scorpius zodiac sign

Short for "Merope", the youngest of the Pleiades sisters

Short for "Sterope", one of the Pleiades sisters

Astrological characteristics of a person born under the Sagittarius zodiac sign

According to Greek mythology, Scorpius stung and killed Orion.

Stera took over. "Well, Ori was hitting on all of us like usual. But he started to get out of hand. Tau was keeping a watchful eye on Ori, but even so, Scott is an assertive guy and gave Ori a piece of his mind. Whatever he said must have stung. I don't think they've spoken or even been in the same place together since."

Orion can only be seen in the southern celestial hemisphere during the southern hemisphere's winter months, and Scorpius can only be seen during the summer months. Thus you can never seen them in the sky at the same time. According to Greek mythology, Scorpius is said to be chasing Orion away.

"It more than stung. Scott killed Ori." Gomez dropped to the group's gasps. "But now, who killed Scott? Someone who wanted vengeance for Ori's death. Someone physically close to Scott."

A reference to the "declination" coordinate pinpointing where Sagittarius is in the sky

A reference to the "right ascension" coordinate pinpointing where Sagittarius is in the sky

Sagittarius is situated just to the east of Scorpius.

A distant bell chimed 1900 hours. A gust of seawind chilled the air, like the temperature had suddenly plunged to -25 degrees. Gomez's walkie talkie screeched with a strong, piercingly loud radio signal. Out of nowhere, a beast-like man with a bow and arrow lunged out of the bushes towards the sisters. Before any damage could be done, ever-watchful Tau tackled him to...

According to one version of Greek mythology, Sagittarius stands ready to attack Scorpius to avenge Orion's death.

A reference to Sagittarius A, the strong radio source at the center of the galaxy that lies within the Sagittarius constellation

Sagittarius is typically depicted as a centaur with a bow and arrow.

...he scales of justice are up there with Scott tonight."

...ed, remembering the friends they lost. "What consolation is t...

A reference to the constellation Libra, the "scales of justice", that are situated just to the west of Scorpius

Sounds like "constellation". Therefore the sisters are asking what constellation is represented by the beast-like man known as SGR, the answer being: Sagittarius.

Sagittarius

I Can Has Obscure Book?

You didn't think I'd really leave you one Theorem short, did you? Appropriate to the subject matter, your answer is in plain sight—or will be once you know what to look for.

To solve this Theorem, make life imitate art and physically type the URL shown above this innocent-looking cat into a browser on your computer, where you'll find the very same picture of said cat. Now, remember that I hinted at tinkering with the color information in photos? And how I cleverly (awkwardly?) used the term "contrast" quite a bit? Taken all together, that should clue you in to the fact that you'll need to change the contrast on that image to find your hidden message.

Do that by either using the controls on your computer screen or editing the image directly with photo editing software. After a little trial and error you'll find that by cranking the contrast all the way up, the word STEGACAT appears right above that adorable fluffball's head.

I gave that nickname to a stray cat who frequents my house when he started leaving hidden "messages" in my yard last year. Very subtle, Stega.

My Bread and Butter

Cooking really is my bread and butter. We go together like peanut butter and jelly, like rice and beans, like biscuits and gravy.

All my talk about foods and flavors that go well together should tip you off that you should be looking for classic food pairings. For each item on the left, find the item it perfectly pairs with on the right. For example, spaghetti goes really well with meatballs, and you can't have bacon without eggs.

I also talked about cooking scientifically and the importance of precisely weighing all of your ingredients to make sure things come out just right.

So, "weigh" the components of each pair using the scale at bottom of the image. Put the item from the left side on the left side of the scale and the item from the right on the right. You'll find their weights listed on their packaging. Based on that, imagine how much the needle would move to either the left or right. For example, the peanut butter weighs 459g and the jelly weighs 453g with a 6g difference, meaning the scale needle would move 6 dots to the left.

Given that there are 13 dots to the left on the scale and 13 dots to the right for a total of 26, you might guess that these represent the 26 letters of the alphabet. That diamond at the center that marks a balanced scale represents the space between M and N. So, 6 dots to the left equals 6 letters to the left of the center of M/N in the alphabet, or an H.

After doing the rest in the order the items appear at left, you'll find the answer is HEART AND SOUL, which is what I always put into all of my cooking—no matter how cliché.

The Crown Jewels of Colouring

I said you needed to give your brain a break, so there's not a lot of thought involved here—no codes, no ciphers, no clever allusions to obscure topics. All you have to do is color. Really!

So grab some colored pencils or markers and fill in the shapes according to the key at bottom. All shapes with a 1 inside should be blue, all shapes with a 2 should be orange, and so on and so forth.

This should be fun and relaxing to do. But I have to confess I didn't go through all this effort just to help you destress. When you're done you should notice something unusual about the color patterns. Take a few steps back, maybe squint a little to bring it all together, and you should see the answer: KEEP CALM AND PUZZLE ON.

Just like those unflappable Brits, when the puzzles get tough, you just have to keep carrying on.

Foraging 101

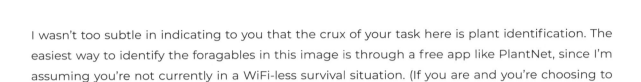

I wasn't too subtle in indicating to you that the crux of your task here is plant identification. The easiest way to identify the foragables in this image is through a free app like PlantNet, since I'm assuming you're not currently in a WiFi-less survival situation. (If you are and you're choosing to solve these Theorems I both applaud your dedication and question your priorities.)

Anyway, download the app and get to foraging! To identify a plant in this wilderness scene, snap a picture with the in-app camera. Be sure to get a clear, closeup shot. When looking at the list of possible matches, note that the very first result might not be the one you're looking for. The right one, which could be a slightly different species than the top result, might be down one or two in the list.

Now start filling out the foraging journal I've provided you. Next to each plant's depiction, write in its scientific name, meaning genus and species (remember I told you never to use common names!). Then enter the count of each plant you see in the column labeled with a # to ensure you're not over-harvesting. Next, note if the plant is edible or toxic by placing either a check mark or an X in the column labeled with a fork and knife. Do this for all 10 plants.

For example, the third line in your journal refers to the *Taxus baccata* plant, of which there are six in this scene. A quick Google search will tell you that it is most definitely not edible.

Now, use the number of each plant you encountered to index into (i.e. "pick" letters from) the scientific names. So, to continue our example, there are six *Taxus baccata* plants and the sixth letter of TAXUS BACCATA is B.

The letters you wind up with—ELBEDRREYR—may seem like a jumble, but when you remember to separate the edible plants (or letters) from the toxic ones, you get ELDER and BERRY, or ELDERBERRY, which is the answer.

Elderberry (or *Sambucus*) is a genus that keeps you on your toes. Many species are both edible (the berries) and toxic (the stems and the rest of the plant). So, like I said, you better know exactly what you're picking up in the wild.

	#	🍴?			#	🍴?
 MYOSOTIS SCORPIOIDES	18	✓	BRUGMANSIA SUAVEOLENS	2	✗	
TYPHA LATIFOLIA	6	✓	NERIUM OLEANDER	3	✗	
TAXUS BACCATA	6	✗	ECHINACEA PURPUREA	8	✓	
AGERATINA ALTISSIMA	3	✗	ACTAEA PACHYPODA	11	✗	
DAUCUS CAROTA	1	✓	VERBENA HASTATA	3	✓	

ELDERBERRY

The Minor Theorem

This may look complicated, but take it slow! Anyone can do math if you break it down step by step.

Don't let the axioms throw you. All they really say is that we're going to be writing a bunch of numbers arranged with colons between them, and then we're also going to write a bunch of those colon-separated numbers arranged with double arrows between them. There's no real reason why, it's just the notation we'll be using here.

The rest of the symbols are just saying that we're going to be converting these numbers to letters, and then those letters to words, and then those words (which happen to be words for numbers) back to letters.

The definition of $\omega(\theta_1)$ in the first part of The Minor Theorem just says to convert each number in the first set of colon-separated numbers directly to letters. With 20 = T, 23 = W, and so on, we get TWELVE.

The definition of $\omega(\theta_\beta)$ then says that for all the rest of the colon-separated numbers, you also convert them to letters, but shifted right in the alphabet by the value of the number word before it (wrapping around to the beginning of the alphabet after you pass Z). Since the first word we got was TWELVE, we add twelve to 20, 23, 10, and 19, then convert to letters to get FIVE.

The next set of numbers then gets shifted right by five to get THIRTEEN, the next set gets shifted by thirteen to get THIRTEEN again, then the last set gets shifted right by thirteen to get ONE.

The corollary to The Minor Theorem says to simply convert all the number words you got directly to letters. With 12, 5, 13, 13, and 1 that gives LEMMA, the answer.

A lemma, of course, is a helper theorem that doesn't really have much use or applicability except towards the ends of solving another more important theorem. Kind of like how this Minor Theorem I made up is totally useless, except that it is helping you solve The Master Theorem.

$$\theta_1 \qquad\qquad \theta_2 \qquad\qquad\qquad \theta_3 \qquad\qquad\qquad\qquad \theta_4 \qquad\qquad \theta_5$$

20::23::5::12::22::5 >> 20::23::10::19 >> 15::3::4::13::15::26::26::9 >> 7::21::22::5::7::18::18::1 >> 2::1::18

$\omega(\theta_1) = \lambda(20)\ \lambda(23)\ \lambda(5)\ \lambda(12)\ \lambda(22)\ \lambda(5)$
$\qquad\qquad = TWELVE$

TWELVE >> 20::23::10::19 >> 15::3::4::13::15::26::26::9 >> 7::21::22::5::7::18::18::1 >> 2::1::18

$\omega(\theta_1)$ $\qquad\quad \mu(TWELVE) = 12$
$\qquad\qquad\quad +12 = 32::35::22::31$
$\qquad\qquad\quad \delta(\eta) = 6::9::22::5$
$\qquad\qquad\quad \omega(\theta_2) = \lambda(6)\ \lambda(9)\ \lambda(22)\ \lambda(5)$
$\qquad\qquad\qquad\quad = FIVE$

TWELVE >> FIVE >> 15::3::4::13::15::26::26::9 >> 7::21::22::5::7::18::18::1 >> 2::1::18

$\omega(\theta_1)$ $\qquad\quad \omega(\theta_2)$ $\qquad\quad \mu(FIVE) = 5$
$\qquad\qquad\qquad\qquad\quad +5 = 20::8::9::18::20::31::31::14$
$\qquad\qquad\qquad\qquad\quad \delta(\eta) = 20::8::9::18::20::5::5::14$
$\qquad\qquad\qquad\qquad\quad \omega(\theta_3) = \lambda(20)\ \lambda(8)\ \lambda(9)\ \lambda(18)\ \lambda(20)\ \lambda(5)\ \lambda(5)\ \lambda(14)$
$\qquad\qquad\qquad\qquad\qquad\quad = THIRTEEN$

TWELVE >> FIVE >> THIRTEEN >> 7::21::22::5::7::18::18::1 >> 2::1::18

$\omega(\theta_1)$ $\qquad\quad \omega(\theta_2)$ $\qquad\quad \omega(\theta_3)$ $\qquad\quad \mu(THIRTEEN) = 13$
$\qquad\qquad\qquad\qquad\qquad\qquad\qquad +13 = 20::34::35::18::20::31::31::14$
$\qquad\qquad\qquad\qquad\qquad\qquad\qquad \delta(\eta) = 20::8::9::18::20::5::5::14$
$\qquad\qquad\qquad\qquad\qquad\qquad\qquad \omega(\theta_4) = \lambda(20)\ \lambda(8)\ \lambda(9)\ \lambda(18)\ \lambda(20)\ \lambda(5)\ \lambda(5)\ \lambda(14)$
$\qquad\qquad\qquad\qquad\qquad\qquad\qquad\quad = THIRTEEN$

TWELVE >> FIVE >> THIRTEEN >> THIRTEEN >> 2::1::18

$\omega(\theta_1)$ $\qquad\quad \omega(\theta_2)$ $\qquad\quad \omega(\theta_3)$ $\qquad\qquad\quad \omega(\theta_4)$ $\qquad\quad \mu(THIRTEEN) = 13$
$\qquad\qquad\qquad\qquad\qquad\qquad\qquad\qquad\qquad\qquad +13 = 15::14::31$
$\qquad\qquad\qquad\qquad\qquad\qquad\qquad\qquad\qquad\qquad \delta(\eta) = 15::14::5$
$\qquad\qquad\qquad\qquad\qquad\qquad\qquad\qquad\qquad\qquad \omega(\theta_5) = \lambda(15)\ \lambda(14)\ \lambda(5)$
$\qquad\qquad\qquad\qquad\qquad\qquad\qquad\qquad\qquad\qquad\qquad = ONE$

TWELVE >> FIVE >> THIRTEEN >> THIRTEEN >> ONE

$\omega(\theta_1)$ $\qquad\quad \omega(\theta_2)$ $\qquad\quad \omega(\theta_3)$ $\qquad\qquad\quad \omega(\theta_4)$ $\qquad\quad \omega(\theta_5)$

$\phi = \lambda(\mu(TWELVE))\ \lambda(\mu(FIVE))\ \lambda(\mu(THIRTEEN))\ \lambda(\mu(THIRTEEN))\ \lambda(\mu(ONE))$
$\quad = \lambda(12)\ \lambda(5)\ \lambda(13)\ \lambda(13)\ \lambda(1)$

$$= LEMMA$$

In the Eye of the Beholder

Remember how I said Renaissance masters' eyes for detail were like magic? Well, the painting in this image is the classic *School of Athens* by Raphael, but modified to be a classic Magic Eye illusion (otherwise known to my lawyers by the unbranded term "autostereogram").

These things can be tricky. To resolve all that visual noise into a picture, you need to bring your nose really close to it and stare as though you're looking through the image. Then draw your face back slowly and a 3D image appears! Now, you may need to practice a few times on easier images, so look at a few online before coming back to here. I'll wait.

Okay, ready?

Do what you just learned on this image, and you'll see the answer, PERSPECTIVE, hovering in 3D above that Raphael painting most famous for its notable use of a Renaissance technique called perspective projection.

The School of Athens was painted more than 300 years before the first photograph was printed. Doesn't that put things into, shall I say... perspective?

PERS PECT IVE

The School of Athens
by Raphael
(a digital reproduction)

Grandpre, Je t'aime

My not-so-subtle misspelling of "Grand Prix" as "Grandpre" should be a tip off. If you do a little googling, you'll realize there's a thing called the Grandpré cipher.

The Grandpré cipher uses between six and ten 6-10 letter words arranged in a square such that the first letters of each spell another master keyword. In this case we are using ten 10-letter words plus an eleventh 10-letter master key.

You may notice there are eleven all-uppercase words in the ads behind the race track. A sharp eye will tell you that FLASHPOINT is the master key—since, of course, they are the master key makers. You can quickly confirm this by realizing that the other ten words each start with a different letter from FLASHPOINT.

To get started, draw a 10x10 square of boxes and put FLASHPOINT down the first column. Across each row, put one of the other 10-letter words from the ads that start with the corresponding letter of FLASHPOINT. That would make the first row FEDERATION and the last row TRADEMARKS. You can see the full square in the image at right.

Now label each row and column 0-9. (Some Grandpré ciphers use 1-9 with a 0 at the end, but here we use 0-9 as indicated by the "0-9 days" boast in the FLASHPOINT ad.)

You should notice that each racecar is labeled with a double-digit number, which also happens to be what the ciphertext of a Grandpré cipher looks like. Write them out in the order the cars appear in the race, starting with the car in first place. The first number in each double-digit represents the row in our grid and the second represents the column. So the 0th row and 0th column translates to F in our grid, and the 9th row and 1st column is R, and so on.

Following this logic through to the end gives you the answer: FRANCE.

France has great ties to both car racing and ciphers. In that first auto race in 1894, drivers sped from Paris to Rouen. France was also the home country of the creator of the Grandpré cipher. And the founder of NASCAR was Bill France!

Et voilà! Vive la France et les chiffrement.

79 = E 64 = C 28 = N 35 = A 00 = F 91 = R

	0	1	2	3	4	5	6	7	8	9
0	F	E	D	E	R	A	T	I	O	N
1	L	A	N	D	S	C	A	P	E	S
2	A	N	T	I	T	O	X	I	N	S
3	S	U	N	G	L	A	S	S	E	S
4	H	E	L	I	C	O	P	T	E	R
5	P	E	N	T	A	Q	U	A	R	K
6	O	B	J	E	C	T	I	V	L	Y
7	I	N	I	T	I	A	L	I	Z	E
8	N	E	W	S	P	A	P	E	R	S
9	T	R	A	D	E	M	A	R	K	S

World-Wide Wanderings

I've given you a haphazard map of my world-wide wanderings. You need to find your way from the beginning (the hiker icon at left) all the way to the end (the hiker icon at right).

I mentioned that I post pictures of my travels at every step along the way to Instagram, so I'd be pretty offended if you didn't immediately go check out my profile. There's a link in the footer at **http://themastertheorem.com** if you couldn't find me otherwise.

Head to the very beginning of my feed. You'll notice the pictures resemble the icons on my map indicating what I saw along each path. Use the pictures to figure out the consecutive series of paths I took to get from the beginning to the end.

For example, the first picture in my feed is of a waterfall, so I went down path T first (it depicts a waterfall). The next picture is a rock tunnel, so I took path W (the one with the rock tunnel) after that. The next picture is of flowers, which could either mean I went down path O to the left or path I to the right. But the picture after that is of a cabin, so that must mean I went down path O then path R, since the photos are from one trail (I haven't yet perfected teleportation so I can't jump around in space).

When you encounter a path with multiple icons on it make sure you choose the path that corresponds to the matching order of pictures seen in my feed. For example, in the river, I picked the upper path because the images in my feed are of a lilypad, fish, and bird in that order.

Keep going until you get to the exit of the map at right. Collect all the path names you've encountered along the way and it spells, TWO ROADS DIVERGED IN A WOOD AND I, I TOOK THE ONE LESS TRAVELED BY. You may recognize what that's from, but if you don't—that's what Google is for. It's part of a poem by Robert Frost called THE ROAD NOT TAKEN which is the answer and my general philosophy, whether wandering the world or making life choices.

Dreamland Textures

My brain may be complicated but this Theorem isn't.

The textures you see here are based on patterns that simply look like letters. For example, that first one which looks like stone steps kind of has a V-shaped vibe to it. That next one with feathers looks a lot like a whole bunch of bubbly, uppercase Es.

Keep going down the image and you'll find that it spells VELVETY—a Nat King Cole song. A Creme Brulee. That satisfying feeling of catching the bad guy. The texture of my life.

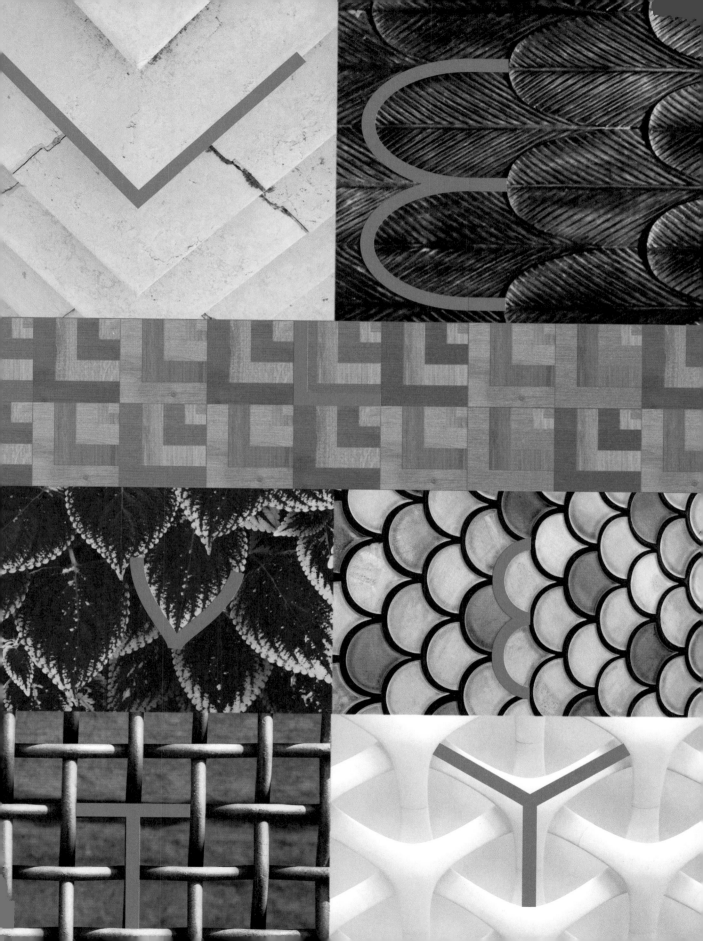

Of Thee I Sing

Between my talk about turning up the music, turning what's on the grille, and my misspelling of the word "grill", you should catch on that we're working with a turning grille cipher here. Or if that was too subtle for your googling abilities, you might also have noticed that the brand name of my grill is "Fleissner"—Fleissner grille cipher being another name for the turning grille cipher.

Turning grille ciphers involve encoding text using a (typically 8x8) grid and a similarly sized sheet with precisely cut holes in it—otherwise known as a grille. The text is encoded by writing the plaintext one letter at a time through the holes, turning the grille 90 degrees, and repeating the process four times (hence the nickname "turning grille cipher"). What you end up with is a grid filled with completely jumbled letters of the original plaintext.

To decode, you just need the grid of letters and the grille that was used to encode. It should be pretty easy to identify the grid here: it's that stuff on the Post-it note on my radio. ID'ing the grille requires a little more sleuthing. Hang on, do you want cheese on your burger?

Notice that the holes in the Swiss cheese and the letters on the Post-it are both 8x8 grids. So use the pattern of holes in the Swiss cheese as your grille to overlay on top of the Post-it, and pull out the letters that show through top to bottom and left to right. You'll get: I GOT MY HANDS UP THE. Now turn the cheese grille (not the grid of letters) 90 degrees clockwise and do this again. This gives you: Y'RE PLAYIN' MY SON. Keep turning and reading out letters as shown at right, and this eventually all spells out: I GOT MY HANDS UP, THEY'RE PLAYIN' MY SONG, YOU KNOW I'M GONNA BE OKAY. YEAH IT'S A ...

If that song lyric doesn't already sound familiar to you, then you obviously were not heavy in the club scene circa 2009. It's from Miley Cyrus's song PARTY IN THE USA, which completes the quote and is the answer to this star-spangled Theorem.

July 4th Playlist

I GOT MY HANDS UP, THE

90°

July 4th Playlist

Y'RE PLAYIN' MY SON

90°

July 4th Playlist

G, YOU KNOW I'M GONNA

90°

July 4th Playlist

BE OKAY. YEAH IT'S A ...

PARTY IN THE USA

July 4th Playlist

G R M Y   B Y I I   ' O   E
  M   Y   G B U H   I L   T N A   O E K
Y I   K O A   P O A N I W H   A ' Y Y N G
  M U   O A ' I S O A N S A   P D Y   E S
U   O   T A   A A N H   N   N ...   S E

Monstrous Math

Maybe you can see why my marketing team told me to nix this idea, but this version of the game still has a special place in my heart.

Get your mathematician's hat on and start playing the old version of Adsumudi as I've described it. You're looking to form a valid equation using only sines, moduluses, exponents, and logarithms. For each of the eight cards, a player has already shouted a valid equation with blanks where the numbers go. Your job is to use the five numbers on each card (using each number only once!) to fill in the five blanks in each equation so that you end up with a positive, whole number answer.

To avoid any crazy decimal answers, you'll have to work smart. For each equation, there should only be one valid arrangement of the numbers in the blanks that come out with a round number, and you can work your way towards that by process of elimination.

For example, in the first equation, the only two numbers that can practically go in the log are 4 and 16 since 16 is an even power of 4. The only number that can go in the $\sin^{-1}$ would be ½ (if you look up a sine chart, anything else would give you a long decimal). And so that only leaves 49 and ½ to use as the base and exponent at left respectively, which works because 49 is a square number, the square

root of which is the nice round number 7. Plug all that in and it gives you a nice round 19 as your target number.

You can see how all the others fill out at right, but if you're stubborn and want to do it on your own, here are some tips that'll help you:

- Be familiar with common sine values like those for 0°, 30°, 45°, 60°, 90°, and 270°
- Any number raised to a negative exponent flips the base into a fraction (i.e. 2^{-1} = ½ and 2^{-2} = ¼)
- An exponent of ½ is a square root (i.e. $16^{½}$ = 4)
- The log of a number with a base of the same number equals 1 (i.e. $\log_{45}(45)$ = 1)
- The log of a power of the base simply equals the power (i.e. $\log_4(4^{32})$ = 32)

Using these, you end up with the target numbers for each card shown at right, which when translated to letters spells the answer, SIMOEXLO. That's the original name of the game, featuring the first two letters of the allowed math functions (SIne, MOdulus, EXponent, LOgarithm).

I guess, to be fair, Adsumudi rolls off the tongue a little easier. Maybe those marketing folks know what they're doing after all.

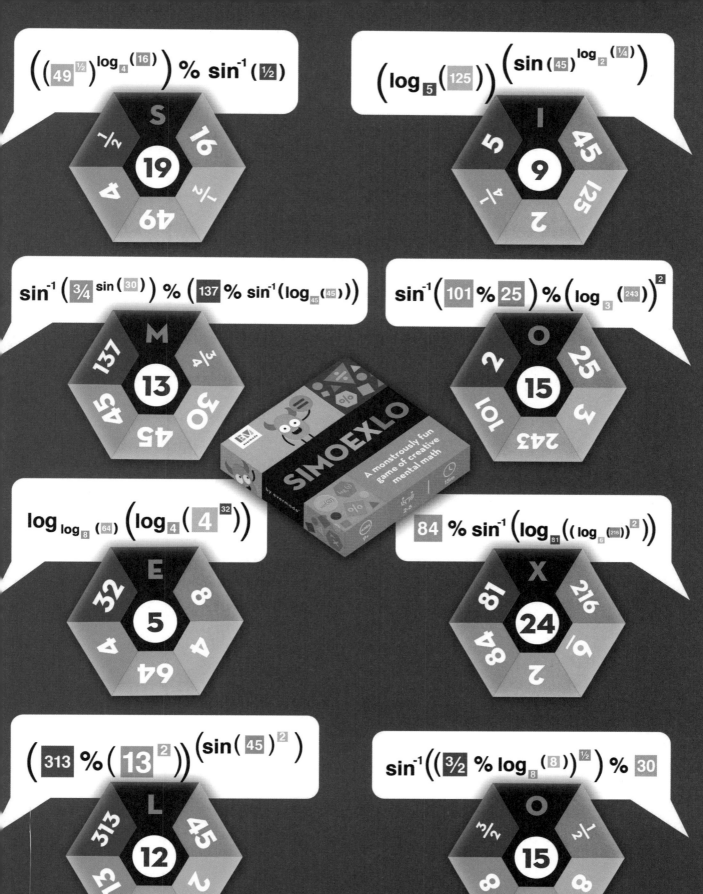

The Right to Write

You may be familiar with ciphers of this format from the puzzle section of your favorite newspaper. It's called a "cryptoquote." If you hadn't seen something like this before, you could also get the gist from the big quotation marks and a bit of googling.

A cryptoquote is essentially a substitution cipher in which a famous quote is encoded by replacing each letter with another letter. Through some educated guessing and logical deduction, you get to spend a joyful Sunday afternoon decoding it, then basking in the wisdom of the quoted author.

Here, I've leveled up the classic puzzle by using a homophonic substitution cipher instead of just a regular one. In a homophonic substitution cipher, a single plaintext letter is represented by multiple other letters or symbols, called homophones, which makes it all the more difficult to decode. But I've given you a leg up here by tapping into my love of language and making the replacements *actual* homophones. By which I mean all the words that sound the same map to one letter in the plaintext quote.

With that knowledge in your arsenal, solve this like a regular cryptoquote. You'll have to start with some educated guesses. For example, that first three letter word is most likely "the," the most common three-letter word in English. So that would mean all the words that sound like "rose" ("rose," "rows," "rhos," and "roes") are Ts and all the words that sound like "their" ("their," "there," and "they're") are Hs, and so on. Keep making guesses based on context, backtracking when you need to, until all the blanks are filled out.

When you're done, it should spell out the quote from Lewis CAROL's *Through the Looking-Glass*, as seen at right. (CAROL being your final answer.)

And yes, calm down, I know Lewis' last name is "Carroll" and not "Carol," but when I reed about Alice's wacky adventures, I'm transported back to my wintry childhood Christmas daze, going door to door singing about the Cheshire Cat leading Santa's slay. Was that won not a classic in yore house?

"THE QUESTION IS "
ROSE THEIR CARROT FOR SEA KARAT T'S ROWS PRAISE BUY YOU PRAYS TEAS ,

SAID ALICE ,
TEASE MEDAL PREYS TWO METAL CENTS PRAYS OUR CARET

" WHETHER YOU CAN
NOSE THERE CARAT RHOS THEY'RE KARAT YOUR ONE BYE SEE HOUR MEDDLE U

MAKE WORDS MEAN
AISLE METTLE AFFECT CARET NO'S BY YORE TO TEES I'LL CARROT METAL EWE

SO MANY DIFFERENT
TEASE BY ISLE MEDAL YEW WON TOO PRAISE WHICH WITCH CARROT YOU'RE KARAT U ROSE

THINGS . "
ROES THERE PREYS YOU WHERE T'S

— LEWIS CAROL IN
SCENTS CARAT KNOWS PRAYS TEAS PRAISE YEW

THROUGH THE
RHOS THEIR YOUR BYE C WEAR THEY'RE ROSE THERE KARAT

LOOKING - GLASS
SENSE BUY BYE EFFECT PRAISE EWE WHERE WARE CENTS MEDDLE TEAS TEASE

Einstein's Greatest Puzzle

This classic logic puzzle is called an Einstein puzzle, due to the fact that many believe the format was invented by Einstein himself. In an Einstein puzzle, you are given a series of clues to help you figure out how certain features match up with one another.

In this one, you have to figure out what relativistic speeds, time dilations, and length contractions each spice-collecting spaceship experienced given the clues listed in the business observational log.

To solve an Einstein puzzle, it's easiest to create a chart to keep track of the information you learn from the clues. For this puzzle, make a 15x15 grid with the five length contractions, five time dilations, and five speeds respectively across the top, and the five ship names, five speeds, and five time dilations respectively down the left. (Ignore the three redundant 5x5 blocks at bottom right.) You can find the full recommended set-up at right.

So, start filling in the chart! For example, the first clue says that the ship that experienced an 8m length contraction also experienced a 2h time dilation, so you would put a check mark where the 8m column intersects with the 2h row, and also X's for all other time dilations in the 8m column and all other length contractions in the 2h row.

Keep going. When you think there's nothing else to do, you may have to get clever and make inferences from what you already know. For example, if you know that the ship that experienced an 8m length contraction experienced a 2h time dilation, and also that the ship that was traveling at 65% the speed of light experienced an 8m length contraction, then you know that the ship traveling at 65% the speed of light experienced a 2h time dilation.

Once you've got everything in your chart, note the markings on each ship surrounding the ship name. It's an indication that you should use the time dilation experienced by each ship to index into (expand into) each ship name starting at the beginning. And you should use the length contraction experienced by each ship to index into (shrink into) each ship name from the end. For example, Parsley by the Parsec experienced a 4h time dilation and 6m length contraction, which translates to an S (4th letter from beginning) and a P (6th letter from end).

Grab all the letters from each ship and this spells SPACETHYME, your answer and the best relativistic-speed spice running ship since the Millenium Falcon. Bet it could do the Kessel Run in less than 10 parsecs. Take that, Han!

		Length Contraction					Time Dilation					Speed				
		4m	6m	8m	14m	15m	2h	4h	5h	8h	15h	50%	55%	60%	65%	70%
Ship Name	PARSLEY BY THE PARSEC	✗	✓	✗	✗	✗	✗	✓	✗	✗	✗	✗	✓	✗	✗	✗
	MINTERGALACTIC	✓	✗	✗	✗	✗	✗	✗	✗	✓	✗	✗	✗	✗	✗	✓
	THE SEED OF LIGHT	✗	✗	✗	✓	✗	✗	✗	✓	✗	✗	✗	✗	✓	✗	✗
	THE MILKY CARAWAY	✗	✗	✓	✗	✗	✓	✗	✗	✗	✗	✗	✗	✗	✓	✗
	EARTH TO CARDAMOM	✗	✗	✗	✗	✓	✗	✗	✗	✗	✓	✓	✗	✗	✗	✗
Speed	50%	✗	✗	✗	✗	✓	✗	✗	✗	✗	✓					
	55%	✗	✓	✗	✗	✗	✗	✓	✗	✗	✗					
	60%	✗	✗	✗	✓	✗	✗	✗	✓	✗	✗					
	65%	✗	✗	✓	✗	✗	✓	✗	✗	✗	✗					
	70%	✓	✗	✗	✗	✗	✗	✗	✗	✓	✗					
Time Dilation	2h	✗	✗	✓	✗	✗										
	4h	✗	✓	✗	✗	✗										
	5h	✗	✗	✗	✓	✗										
	8h	✓	✗	✗	✗	✗										
	15h	✗	✗	✗	✗	✓										

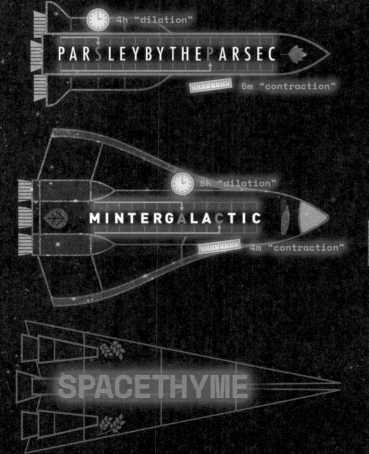

PARSLEYBYTHEPARSEC — 4h "dilation" — 6m "contraction"

MINTERGALACTIC — 8h "dilation" — 4m "contraction"

SPACETHYME

THESEEDOFLIGHT — 5h "dilation" — 14m "contraction"

THEMILKYCARAWAY — 2h "dilation" — 8m "contraction"

EARTHTOCARDAMOM — 15h "dilation" — 15m "contraction"

Aboriginal

Learning about Aboriginal origin stories made me wonder how other types of origin stories might be represented, too. So, all of the drawings here depict well-known origin stories (at least, from western pop culture). For example, the top left illustration depicts the origins of SUPERMAN fleeing an exploding planet as a baby. The middle right illustration depicts the Tower of Babel which is known as the origin of LANGUAGE, and the bottom right depicts the origins of the UNIVERSE in the big bang.

Identify each, write them in the blanks, pick out the letters that have tick mark numbers beneath them, and order the letters by those numbers.

Doing this gives you INVASION DAY, which is what many Aboriginal people (and an increasing number of non-Aboriginal people) call Australia Day—a reframing of the holiday from a day of celebration to one of mourning it.

Special thanks to Dixon Patten, a proud Yorta Yorta and Gunnai man, for the phenomenal artwork on this one.

Everyone Hates Moral Philosophy Professors

A nihilistic life may sometimes be devoid of meaning, but my ramblings that accompany each Theorem never are. Take my talk of nihilism as a hint that you're dealing with a Nihilist cipher.

To encrypt a Nihilist cipher, you need two keys: one to generate a 5x5 grid called a polybius square, and one to use in an additive step that further encrypts your plaintext.

So to decrypt, you obviously need to know what those keys are. Well, the "key works" of philosophy on these shelves aren't just my suggestions for your reading list; the two with "key" symbols on them are your keys to this cipher. The first is Plato's *Republic*. With its key and plus sign symbols, it's telling you that REPUBLIC is the keyword to use in the additive step. The second is Aristotle's *Metaphysics*. Its key and grid symbols mean you should use METAPHYSICS to create your polybius square.

Start by creating your grid. Begin at the top left box and fill in the letters of METAPHYSICS without repeating any letters. You'll end up with METAPHYSIC. Then fill in the rest of the grid with the rest of the letters of the alphabet in order. As noted by the "i/j" also on the *Metaphysics* book, you'll be using the most common variation of the polybius square where the I and J reside in the same box (so

don't give J its own square). See at right for the full set up.

Then, using the grid, translate REPUBLIC into two-digit numbers with the row number as the first digit and column number as the second. So R, for example, translates to 45.

Then, one by one, subtract subsequent numbers from REPUBLIC from the ciphertext numbers, then translate the result back into a letter using the grid. For example, subtracting 45 (the R from REPUBLIC) from 59 (the number on the first piece of paper) gives 14, which translates to an A in the 1st row and 4th column of the grid. You can see the rest at right.

Keep going and this spells ACTIVE NIHILISM, your answer and the philosophy that I feel best aligns with my own worldview. I think nihilism has it right insofar as there is no objective point or values or morals in life. But the deep despair that this realization initially brings can be overcome by recognizing that you have the freedom to create your own values and live your life in a way that makes you happy.

After all, what is the point of living if not to be happy? Don't answer that, Chidis of the world. Let me have this one.

1 2 3 4 5

	1	2	3	4	5
↓ 1 →	M	E	T	(A)	P
2	H	Y	S	I	C
3	B	D	F	G	K
4	L	N	O	Q	R
5	U	V	W	X	Z

R E P U B L I C

45 12 15 51 31 41 24 25

59	37	28	75	83	53
- 45	- 12	- 15	- 51	- 31	- 41
= 14	= 25	= 13	= 24	= 52	= 12
= A	= C	= T	=	= V	= E

ACTIVE

NIHILISM

METAPHYSICS

66	49	66	36	56	75	54	52
- 24	- 25	- 45	- 12	- 15	- 51	- 31	- 41
= 42	= 24	= 21	= 24	= 41	= 24	= 23	= 11
= N	= I	= H	= I	= L	= I	= S	= M

We're the Bomb Squad

If you're an EE sort of person, the components in this detonator circuit may look like real resistors, integrated circuits, inductors, transistors, and 7-segment displays, but they play by their own rules here. Use the diagram at bottom to figure out how they work. Numbers (voltages) travel through lines (wires) unmodified, and change when passing through components. Start with the 9 at top left and work your way towards the four central displays.

According to the diagram, when four numbers (A, B, C, and D) enter a  at left, they come out at right as B-A, DxC, B/2, and A-7 respectively. When four numbers enter a ▒, they come out the right as C/B, A+3, A-10, and BxD. For example, if a 9, 10, 4, and 2 went into a ▲, they would come out as 10 - 9 = 1, 2 x 4 = 8, 10 / 2 = 5, and 9 - 7 = 2 respectively. Note that the orientations of these two chips matter. When the triangle or star icon is pointing upwards, electricity enters at left and leaves at right.

When a number (A) goes into a ▬▐█▬, it comes out the other side as A - X, where the first colored band represents the first digit of X and the second colored band the second digit of X. For example, a ▬▐█▬ has a value of X = 12, because, according to the diagram, brown is 1 and red is 2. So if an 18 went into a ▬▐█▬, it would come out as 18 - 12 = 6.

When a number (A) goes into a ▥, it comes out the other side as A + N, where N is the number of coils. So if a 6 goes into a ▥, it comes out as 6 + 8 = 14.

When three numbers (A, B, and C, A being the central pin) enter a ☀, they come out as B + C if A ≤ 5 or B - C if A > 5. So if a 1, 8, and 9 (where A is 1) went into a ☀, it would come out as 8 + 9 = 17. But if a 6, 12, 1 (where A is 6) went into a ☀ it would come out as 12 - 1 = 11.

Work your way through the circuit until you figure out what all the numbers are that lead into the central four 7-segment LED displays. According to the diagram, a number entering a particular LED display "lights up" the segment labeled with that number. So if a 7 went into one, it would light up the central horizontal segment.

Color in all the segments indicated to light up and it spells BANG, exactly what we wanted to have happen in our lab, and exactly what we didn't want to have happen out in the real world.

A True Type of Murder

I imagine many modern cryptographers got their start sitting at old Windows computers typing secret messages to their friends in Wingdings and Webdings. This whole crime story is an elaborate reference to these fonts, which replace letters and other characters with "ornamental" icons of all sorts—think astrological symbols, hand gestures, circles, diamonds, squares, and more.

They're called "dingbat" fonts, which are also known as "printer's ornament" fonts and were used in typesetting for decorative or spacing purposes.

Between the story's subtle (Charles Bigelow and Kris Holmes were co-creators of Wingdings) and not-so-subtle ("wing—ding! web—ding!") hints, you should be able to figure out what we're working with here. I've highlighted all my hints at right, just in case you missed some.

You can also see at right that the Christmas tree ornaments named during Krissy's interrogation all reference different icons in either Wingdings or Webdings.

If you have these fonts on your computer, type out all the uppercase and lowercase letters in both fonts and take note of the icons that look like any of the ornaments described in the story (otherwise just search online for a chart of the characters).

For example, the Beach Barbie laying under an umbrella refers to the beach icon (a capital "I" in Webdings) and the locomotive on an open air track refers to the diesel locomotive icon (a lowercase "t" in Webdings).

Putting all the letters together, ignoring case, spells: IT WAS THE CAT. That'll do as the answer and our murderer of Spiderman, but there's one more ornament referenced at the end—Spiderman himself! Since a spider is a "!" in Webdings, your final, final answer is not just THE CAT, it's more emphatically, THE CAT!

Pesky little creatures.

A TRUE TYPE OF MURDER

...the night before Christmas 1998 all through the **Bigelow home**, the ...y was enjoying a quiet evening of ...tion. Little **Charlie** and **Krissy** not ...content with the typical array of Christmas tree **ornaments**, adorned branch... Baby **Vincent** decorated br... with crayon **box drawings**. Mr. and Mrs. Bigelow hung a Merry Christmas sign printed in a **strange**, **decorative font**. It truly was a peaceful night full of favorite things.

Until...crash! Bang!

...or som... ...watched ...n action figure slipped from a weak branch. As if in slow motion, he watched it bounce down—its limited edition **1990 jetpack wing** detaching as it caught on a pine needle, its rare **1997 shooting web** fall... off as it ...ped into an ornament hook. No... ...downward momentum and ... ...l tree stand piece by heartbreaking piece. ...e went the **wing—ding**. Then the **web—ding** ...Spiderman lay in pieces on the floor...

...moment of shocked silence, chaos erupted.

"Why'd you d... ...u're such a **dingbat** Krissy!" Charlie shouted through his tears.

"What? I didn't do it!" Krissy shouted back. "Mayb...

Their... ...e battle and sent everyone to bed, but Krissy couldn't stand being accused of a crime she didn't commit. She waited until she heard the tell-tale sign of her parents going to bed—the jingle of their **Microsoft Windows 95** computer booting down—and snuck back out to the living room. ...s on the case.

...y interrogated eac... hand-made toy ornaments on the tree.

"Was it you, Beach Barbie?" she asked ... **laying under a beach umbrella**... to a deni...

"Was it you, train?" she asked the **toy locomotive on an open air track**. It blew its whistle in the negative.

"How about you, boombox? Or you, Hippie Mike?" Neither the **retro speaker pointing leftward** nor the figurine flashing a **peace sign with its hand** admitted to a thing.

... three must have seen *somethin...* ...with the simple **teardrop**-shap... ornament, a mo...l **passenger cruise ship**, and a ... **ambulance** to no avail.

"Ok, **Scorpion! My horoscope** says you kn... something!" The Mortal Kombat action figu... ...ted Krissy question the **city skyline** playset. ...line pointed to the **construction crane** who ... the buck to the **snowflake**.

...owflake! Of cou...! ...ally ...ate! A humble ...nd from its perch ...e, it ...ve seen everything that transpired that...

...she said eagerly, "you're my last ...me **who shattered Spiderman**."

It WAS The CAT!

A reference to Bigelow & Holmes, the typeface design studio that created the Wingdings font, among others.

A reference to Kris Holmes, co-creator of the Wingdings font.

Wingdings and Webdings were developed by Microsoft (Wingdings having been licensed from Bigelow & Holmes), and were included within Windows systems.

A reference to Charles Bigelow, co-creator of the Wingdings font.

Fonts like Wingdings and Webdings are known as dingbat, or "printer's ornament" fonts, due to their decorative characters.

A beach scene with an umbrella is a capital "I" in Webdings.

The diesel locomotive on an open air track (as opposed to the subway train in a tunnel) is a lowercase "t" in Webdings.

A reference to Vincent Connare, co-designer of the Webdings font.

A more direct reference to the "strange" fonts that are Wingdings and Webdings.

Dingbat fonts like Wingdings and Webdings are similar to "box-drawing" characters used in text-based graphical interfaces.

A speaker pointing leftward is a capital "W" in Webdings.

Wingdings was first created in 1990.

A hand gesture of a peace sign is a capital "A" in Wingdings.

Webdings was created later in 1997.

A passenger cruise ship (as opposed to the motorboat) is a capital "T" in Webdings.

A teardrop is a capital "S" in Wingdings.

Wingdings!

Webdings!

An ambulance is a lowercase "h" in Webdings.

Wingdings and Webdings are considered "dingbat" fonts.

A city skyline is a capital "C" in Webdings.

A reference to the astrological symbol for Scorpio, which is a lowercase "e" in Wingdings.

A construction crane is a capital "A" in Webdings.

A snowflake is a capital "T" in Wingdings.

Putting it all together spells, "It WAS The CAT", which gains even more emphasis with an added "!" represented by a spider in Webdings.

Flying High on Ciphers

I think my cipher mash up is ingenious, though my cryptographer friends think I might have made it overly complex what with all the codes on codes on codes.

At least I started you off easy. For the first step, just read the first five lines in plaintext. You'll get: SHIFT REMAINING LETTERS UP BY THREE.

So, go ahead and do that for the last seven rows. For example, that first P becomes an S (three letters up in the alphabet), the B becomes an E, and so on to spell: SERIFS ARE DASHES SANS ARE DOTS CURSIVES ARE SPACE.

Serif fonts are those that have those little knobs hanging off of them, sans serif fonts don't. Start at the beginning of the entire text block and convert each letter to a dot or dash based on the type of their font. Now, is there any language you can think of that communicates in dots and dashes? Look up a Morse code translator, plug in your pattern, and you get: UNDERLINES ARE BRAILLE.

Braille uses a series of raised dots in 2x3 blocks. So group the letters of the statue likewise and think of the underlined letters as the raised bumps. Translate with a braille chart online and you'll get: CASE IS BINARY.

Almost there! Letters in binary are represented as strings of eight 0s and 1s. So, thinking of lowercase letters as 0s and uppercase as 1s, group the digits into eights and decode with what's called an ASCII chart (again, a little googling is your friend).

Ok, that's it, I promise! Your final answer is DAEDALIAN, which appropriately means "ingenious and complex", a recurring theme in my life and art. I'm thinking about making it the title of my autobiography. Well, as soon as I can figure out how to get past all those redactions...

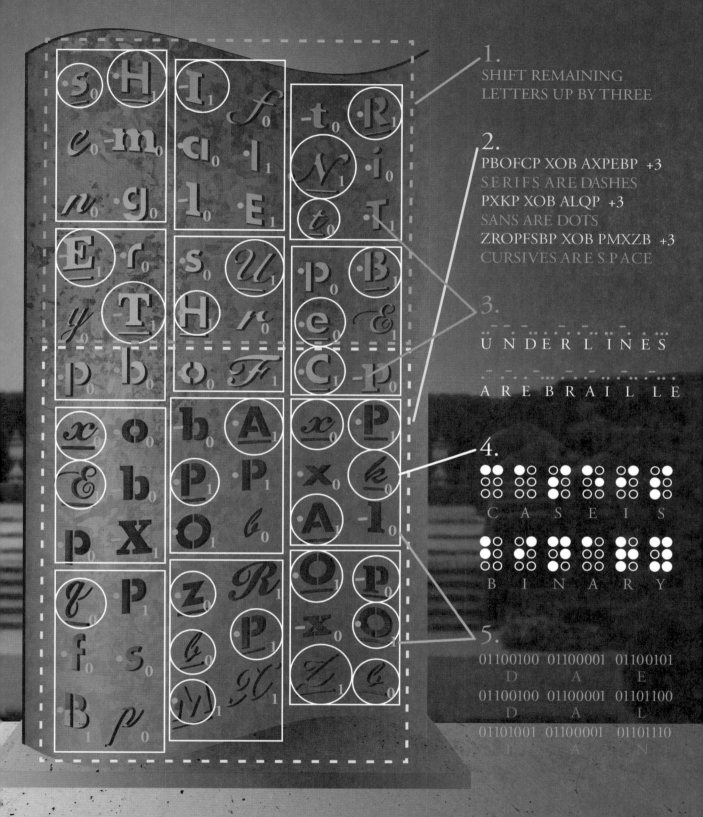

1.
SHIFT REMAINING
LETTERS UP BY THREE

2.
PBOFCP XOB AXPEBP +3
SERIFS ARE DASHES
PXKP XOB ALQP +3
SANS ARE DOTS
ZROPFSBP XOB PMXZB +3
CURSIVES ARE SPACE

3.
UNDERLINES

ARE BRAILLE

4.
CASE IS

BINARY

5.
01100100 01100001 01100101
D   A   E
01100100 01100001 01101100
D   A   L
01101001 01100001 01101110
I   A   N

DAEDALIAN

Escape from TMT, Your Way

So. You're trapped in a room. What are you going to do about it?

You've run with me long enough to know that nothing I do is random. So take careful stock of everything around this escape room. Use all of your past knowledge and experience to get yourself out—meaning, in this case, recalling how you solved the rest of the Theorems in this book.

That bacon branded with a ⊖ looks deliciously familiar right? Recall that I used American bacons as As and back bacons as Bs in a Bacon cipher, and you get BAABB, which translates to a T. Remember when I taught you how to forage? Use an app like PlanetNet to identify the flowers in that picture with the ⅄ on it as *Gaillardia pulchella*. There's eight of them, so take the eighth letter of that and you get D. That floor texture with a ⚡ scratched on it kind of looks like an I, and that Quipu-like strand of knots on the rug embroidered with a 回 sums to 14—so, an N. Those chips and dip with the ♌ go really well together, so weigh them out for a difference of 5g, which would point to an R on my golden scale.

Now that you've got your letters, match them to the symbols in the phone number format on the wall and turn them into an actual phone number using a standard dialpad. You'll get

(646) 434-8768. And since this is an emergency (you're trapped in a room, after all!), dial that phone! Or, rather, dial your actual phone.

Really, give it a call! You'll hear an informant tell you to take *notes* alongside a seemingly nonsensical riddle. So head to the last page of the Notes section in this very book. At the bottom you'll find seven pieces of information. Hey, weren't there seven parts to the riddle, too? Match these up! The informant is coyly telling you that 61 refers to your Grandpré cipher, the colors refer to a neon sign at a pool hall, and the 600 is Chinese yuan that needs to be converted to Brazilian real. "Which", "buy", and "your" are homophones that each map to letters, the skull and crossbones is a Wingdings character, 67 can be thought of as a piece of paper after the final 52 in your Nihilist cipher, and M is a galaxy redshifted by 16 just like galaxy U was.

Solve all that, put it together, and you get BYE FOR NOW, which opens the locks on the door and lets you free.

But you know you'll never be totally free from the mystically alluring book that is *The Master Theorem*.

Until we meet again, dear puzzler, keep doing it the TMT way.

Gaillardia
Pulchella x 8
= D (3 on dialpad)

+5g
= R (7 on dialpad)

CHIPS
+ 691 g

DIP
696g

B A A B B
= T (8 on dialpad)

IN CASE OF EMERGENCY, CALL:
(646) 434-8768

B Y E FOR N O W

61

600

which, buy, your

67

M - 16nm = W

5 + 4 + 8 + 10
= 25 = Y

※ 600 = R$500

FOR
WHICH BUY YOUR

N

67
- 24
= 43
= O

1+1+1+3+3+3+3-1=14
= N (6 on dialpad)

Floor Texture
= I (4 on dialpad)

Notes

"Don't cry because it's over, smile because it happened."

Dr. Seuss